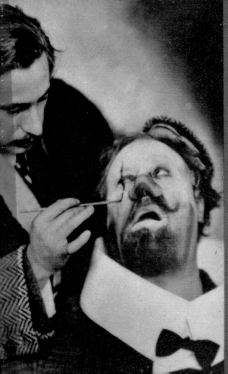

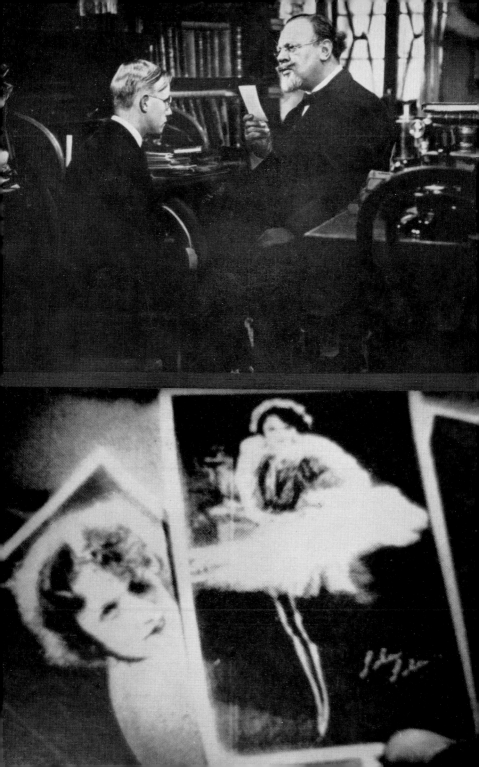

CLASSIC
FILM
SCRIPTS

THE BLUE ANGEL

a film by

Josef von Sternberg

an authorized translation
of the German continuity

Simon and Schuster, New York

General Editor: Sandra Wake

Frontispiece: Josef von Sternberg directing *The Blue Angel*

Library of Congress Catalog Card Number: 68-27595

Manufactured in Great Britain by Villiers Publications Ltd,
London NW5

CONTENTS

ACKNOWLEDGEMENTS

We wish to thank Nicholas Fry for assistance in this book. Our thanks are also due to L'Avant-Scène du Cinéma and the British Film Institute for the use of their stills.

Our deepest thanks and gratitude to Josef von Sternberg, without whom this book could never have been published.

INTRODUCTION

A long while ago, though it seems but yesterday, a steamer no longer in service carried me to a country no longer undivided. This is written in haste, for I am impatient with the past except that ' The memory of past troubles is pleasant.'

Words cannot describe an image in motion, words cannot describe an image. Today *The Blue Angel* is used to describe night clubs, air squadrons and re-makes; before I gave that title to a film it had no existence. An expired passport helps to fix the date. I was dropped at Le Havre on the twelfth of August, 1929, for what was hardly to prove an enjoyable escape from a stint of two years in a Hollywood film factory. I had just finished my first sound film, an indifferent work featuring an actor whose temporary fame was sustained by a so-called silent film called *Underworld*. The entire cast was inferior, all of them unable even to echo my instructions. There was some good warbling in the death row where most of the action took place, but I looked forward with pleasure to making a sound film in Germany. I was not aware, of course, that Europe had only the most primitive method of adding sound to a quite elaborate camerawork which would cause me a lot of trouble. Incidentally, the silent films had never been silent — a piano tinkled, an organ moaned or an orchestra thundered out music that rarely helped the silent film.

This German venture had a curious beginning. I had received a flattering cable from Emil Jannings asking me to guide him in his first sound film, adding that he had the choice of every director on earth but that he preferred me. This touched me deeply, as I had told him in plain language that I would not do another film with him were he the last remaining actor on earth. Once before I had directed him in *The Last Command*, an opus which required him to portray an extra who was called upon to play the part of a commanding general of Russia, a post he had actually had. It was an interesting anatomical survey of the brutality rampant in a motion picture studio. His behaviour interfered with everything I planned. I was slated to do the next film with him, another story by me, *The Street Of Sin*, but I refused and gave the story to Mauritz Stiller. Jannings was impossible to handle, details are in my book. But two years had passed and bygones were bygones, or at least they should have been.

So on a pleasant day in August, I arrived at the Zoo Station in Berlin, to be greeted by a group containing Emil Jannings, Eric Pommer and Karl Vollmoeller. Emil vowed he would be different this time, as indeed he was. Eric Pommer was to be my producer and he was considered an able one. Karl Vollmoeller was a poet and at the time my best friend. Jannings was the one I was to direct. A director's function, if he is to function, is difficult to describe. It embraces a skill in all the arts, though this in itself means little. Every step and every moment is filled with imponderables. 'Trifles light as air' must be ready to become substantial. An audience of one, he controls the camera according to his vision, uses light, shadow and space as his mind dictates, dominates the tempo and content of sound, controls the sets, chooses and edits the actors, decides their appearance and make-up, arranges the scenes in rhythmic progression, eliminates and adds moments that have no meaning to those who stand in attendance, and is solely responsible for every frame of his film. Aside from that he is chief of his crew of workmen, often numbering hundreds though it were better if he managed the giant task of harnessing the cumbersome machine by himself alone. That was my task and this I intended to do. In addition to that I wrote the manuscript on which the theme was based. Now I don't mean to infer that all this permitted me to behave like an angel. Far from it, but my word was law, I was boss, my behaviour was known and this is why I had been called.

After a few friendly exchanges, I asked what the plans were and I was told that the film I was to do was *Rasputin*. I shook my head, this failed to interest me and I suggested that I return to the States. This caused vociferous objections, they would look around for some other idea that would provoke my interest, and I settled down comfortably in a hotel which is now razed and is a pile of rubble behind the ugly wall that divides Berlin.

Among the many subjects and story ideas that were brought to me in the following weeks one caught my fancy. A story by Heinrich Mann, *Professor Unrath*, published in 1905, the locale Lübeck and as any reader of the original can see, a teacher falling in love and marrying a cabaret singer by name of Rosa Fröhlich with child, resigning his position and then using his wife to obtain a footing which enabled him to make a gambling establishment that was to settle his score with society. In conveying the substance of Mann's story to me Jannings was superb, his eyes sparkled, and I began to analyze the ingredients that were to form the basis for *The Blue Angel*.

It took little time for me to make up my mind. Rosa Fröhlich would be Lola-Lola, deprive her of her child, give the pupils intriguing photographs of her, make her heartless and immoral, invent details that are not in the book, and best of all change the role of the teacher to show the downfall of an enamoured man *à la* Human Bondage. None of the distinctive features that fill the film are indicated in the story by Mann. Also not wishing to outrage the author, I asked to see Heinrich Mann. I then told him what changes I contemplated. Mann agreed, saying that he wished he had thought of my ending, and stated that he had no objections to any cinematic devices that might further the story. That was my only contact with the author.

I then gave the go-ahead to the studio and asked for their most able writer to take down my ideas and was given a Herr Robert Liebmann. Next, my immediate concern was the musician, Friedrich Holländer, whom I chose to write songs to fit my plans, a man who had accompanied one of the females proposed by the studio. My next step was to find a designer for the daring costumes I contemplated for the female lead. After rejecting many, I found a talented Hungarian by name of Varady, whose erotic designs were to add so much to the film. His name is absent from the credits of *The Blue Angel*, while many others mentioned are non-contributors. Among those who are mentioned are Karl Vollmoeller and Carl Zuckmayer. Both men were called in to lend their name to the manuscript because it was feared that Germany could not afford the authoring of a German work by a non-German. As a matter of fact, Vollmoeller has denied any authorship, while Zuckmayer in his writings persists in saying that he contributed. He is a brilliant author, but his contributions in *The Blue Angel* are not worth mentioning. However, everyone connected with the film, including the janitor and the night watchman, took pride in the association.

Then after a few cursory glances at the German encyclopaedia, which revealed an uninteresting statistical summary of Lübeck, I started to look around for some woman that could match the ideal creature that I sought. In my book which deals with the problem of directing I mention that the figure looked for was designed by Félicien Rops, a Belgian artist (1833-1897). She was not to be found among the numerous charmers that were paraded in front of me. And I don't mind telling you that many of the women were extremely appealing. But they lacked *das Ewig-Weibliche*. Then on an idle evening I visited a play which contained two actors already chosen, and I noticed a woman on the stage whose face promised everything. This was Marlene Dietrich. I am credited with her discovery. This is not so. I am not an archeologist who finds some buried bones with a pelvis that indicates a female. I am a teacher who took a beautiful woman, instructed her, presented her carefully, edited her charms, disguised her imperfections and led her to crystallize a pictorial aphrodisiac. She was a perfect medium, who with intelligence absorbed my direction, and despite her own misgivings responded to my conception of a female archetype. The balance of the players did as they were told.

But not so Jannings. Curiously enough, in the many books written about and by Emil Jannings, my name is mentioned only once, and incidentally. But that is scarcely the whole story. He was a magnificently bulky man who had the many characters he had portrayed firmly embedded in his person, and had a powerful array of demons everpresent in his makeup. Fat and ungainly, with a complete memory for his own tricks, shifty like a pellet of quicksilver, agile in his repertoire of misbehaviour, he was the perfect actor. His forte was to portray the zenith of personal misfortune; his limpid eyes brimming with misery, he could picture debasement in the most abject terms. To be humiliated was for him ecstasy. Shrewdly aware of his own pranks, powerful as he was as a box-office figure, he would always choose the most formidable directors to restrain and guide him. Aside from his objections to my choice of Dietrich, he opposed me every step of the way. This cannot be seen in the film, even I cannot see it. He gives a competent performance and there is no trace of any obstruction and the untold blocks he laid down to his interpretation and that of the others. As *The Blue Angel* recedes into time, he becomes more and more effective. And that he ended his days as senator of culture for the Nazis (to me he boasted that his mother was a Jewess) will be forgotten long before the perishable celluloid crumbles into ashes.

The set designer, Otto Hunte, endeared himself to me by building a town clock with effective rotating figures; Holländer played the piano and constructed melodies that were irresistable; the cameramen, Rittau and Schneeberger, were fine, and the producer, Eric Pommer, behaved just like a producer should, endorsing my work and visiting the stage only once. The workmen assigned to me were competent. One of them brought his eleven-year-old daughter to watch the scenes and when I objected, saying that she would be corrupted, he remarked *'Ach, die ist ja schon so verdorben!'* (But she is already so corrupt!) And the actors concerned me little when in front of the camera, but as I had taken on the task of being their father for the length of the film, I had to deal with all their problems at home. In one case the young wife of the old sea captain threatened to divorce her husband during the film and when I suggested that she wait until the film was terminated, she screamed that she could no longer put up with her husband whistling when he opened his eyes in bed. This he did, he told me, to assure himself that he was still alive. *Nous dansons sur un volcan.* The filming began sometime in November and finished sometime in December. The year was 1929, Germany was undivided, although the real Germany, its schools and other places pictured in the film were not German and reality failed to interest me.

Film actors, as all students of film history know, are nothing more than glorified marionettes. But unlike a real puppet-master, the director of a film does not manipulate strings on expressionless puppets. For him the dolls are extraordinary personalities who are prone to move every muscle of face and figure to demonstrate every awkward emotion. And when the strings are manoeuvred to present acceptable masks, there is dismay and rebellion. What to reveal and what to conceal is the function of the director. There are standards that go back to the beginning of time. Should anyone ask how to direct a film it would place me in an unenviable position. *Ignotum per ignotius.* It is not possible to give a lucid explanation of the fluid that has to transfer itself to the actors. An alertness and awareness of every moment is essential. The homogeneity of the entire work is constantly at stake. This can only be accomplished by the eye of the camera and by the dangling microphone. Actors are called to the stages to work but a short time. They are costumed, made up, rushed in front of the camera, pose for the adjustment of lights, used but little, and are dismissed. One guides actors in the short time alloted for instruction somehow, by producing perhaps a trance, a sort of mesmerism otherwise unknown, by blotting out their traits and substituting a behaviour alien to them, by gesture and mimicry, by the drama of light and shade, by foiling every obstruction, by movement and angle of the camera, by constant alertness to voice and cadence, and most important of all — by inspecting oneself.

This self-inspection is indeed difficult. At any moment during the working weeks the entire mechanics can take a misleading tangent. The director has no privacy. The stages are littered with many dozens and at times hundreds of others who attack the film-maker with problems and questions that make concentration impossible. Though all are apparently sympathetic, few care anything about directorial labour. And a stream of language from the director is essential. The crew follows orders, but the actor is not part of the crew. Language is hardly the best way to convey ideas and meanings to them. Words trigger wrong ideas, actors retain only words that have a meaning to them. Even when you ' speak to a fool according

14

to his folly ' the reactions stimulated by words are faulty. One says No many times before Yes is heard. And how does one explain abstraction and resonance. And finally, when the actor is no longer present, thousands of feet of film are inspected that can no longer be corrected. Now comes the task of putting tempo and rhythm in what presently glides through a machine that lacks emotion. Disconnected strips of celluloid float by and haunt with their inadequacies. Wince all you like, but that does not alter a single frame. The director is now alone. Cohesion is now made with scissors and cement. To put life into lifeless material is now the task. The harlequinade of making a film is not made easy.

This is an authorised translation of the film continuity in *The Blue Angel*. It was photographed in Berlin during the late winter of 1929. No comprehensive scenario was ever made. Most of the film was improvised on the stages. Its creation, including all difficulties, are mentioned in my book, *Fun in a Chinese Laundry*, published in England by Secker & Warburg in 1966, and in the United States by Macmillan Company in 1965. Very little of the dialogue was in English, and consisted mostly of Berlin slang. Dietrich and Jannings spoke English with each other, in the English version. Both the German and the English version were photographed, one after the other. Little stress was placed on the dialogue, though it is best when understood. As this was the first sound film to be made in Germany, the recording conditions were primitive and dubbing and mixing tracks were not possible.

JOSEF VON STERNBERG

CREDITS:

Directed by	Josef von Sternberg, after a free adaptation of the novel *Professor Unrath,* by Heinrich Mann
Produced by	Erich Pommer
Lyrics and dialogue	Robert Liebmann
Music	Friedrich Holländer
Photography	Günther Rittau, Hans Schneeberger
Sound effects	Fritz Thiery
Décor	Otto Hunte, Emil Hasler
English lyrics	Sam Winston
Courtesy credits	Carl Zuckmayer and Karl Vollmoeller

CAST :

Professor Immanuel Rath	Emil Jannings
Lola-Lola	Marlene Dietrich
Kiepert	Kurt Gerron
Guste, his wife	Rosa Valetti
Mazeppa	Hans Albers
The clown	Reinhold Bernt
The headmaster	Eduard von Winterstein
Angst	Rolf Müller
Lohmann	Roland Verno
Ertzum	Karl Bollhaus
Goldstaub	Robert Klein-Lörk
The proprietor	Karl Huszar-Puffy
The Captain	Wilhelm Diegelmann
The policeman	Gerhard Bienert
Rath's maid	Ilse Fürstenberg
The caretaker	Hans Roth

First shown in Germany	31st March, 1930
Process	Black and white
Screen	1.33/1
Length	2,920 metres

The music is played by	The Weintraubs Syncopators
Songs	' Ich bin die fesche Lola '
	' Kinder, heut' abend such' ich mir was aus '
	' Ich bin von Kopf bis Fuss auf Liebe eingestellt '
	' Nimm dich in Acht vor blonden Frauen '
Music by	Friedrich Holländer
Words by	Robert Liebmann

THE BLUE ANGEL

The screen remains dark for several seconds as music is heard, softly at first and gradually becoming the song 'Ich bin von Kopf bis Fuss' which is the theme-tune of the film. The credits come up in plain white lettering on a black background, at the end of which the music ceases as the first image fades in.

Long shot from above of the steep-pitched roofs and smoking chimneys of an old town. (Still on page 2) Cut to a narrow street: it is early morning and a number of men and women are hauling loudly cackling geese out of cages in preparation for the market. In the background, on the other side of the street, a woman is washing the glass door of a tobacconist's shop. There is a bucket on the ground beside her. Medium shot of the woman from the back as she turns a handle to raise the iron grill over the window. Close-up of the grill rising to reveal a cabaret poster showing a girl in provocative pose with the name 'LOLA-LOLA'. The camera tracks briefly backwards to frame the woman as she picks up the bucket and hurls its water at the window. The poster, being stuck to the inside of the window, remains untouched. The woman starts to wipe the window with a rag, then suddenly pauses to examine the outstretched legs of the girl in the poster. She takes a step backwards, turns towards the camera and, with her eyes still fixed on the poster, clumsily imitates LOLA's *pose.*

Insert in close-up of a plate fixed to a door, which reads 'PR. DR. RATH'.

Long shot of the staircase of a house leading up to the landing, on which the schoolmaster RATH's *apartment is situated. Outside* RATH's *door, a* MAID *takes a bottle of milk from a little girl who hurries past. The girl leaves another bottle at the door of a neighbouring apartment and hurries on up. The* MAID *watches her for a moment and then goes back into* RATH'S *apartment, banging the door behind her.*

In the entrance hall of RATH'S *apartment, the camera pans briefly towards the* MAID, *who goes over to a large mirror and puts down a tray of breakfast things on a small table in front of it. She pours some milk into a jug, lifts the tray and opens a door.*

In RATH'S *study, the door is seen opening from the inside. The* MAID *passes in front of a stove with an old-fashioned flue running right across the room and goes towards another door. She knocks twice.*

MAID : Breakfast, Herr Professor.

Pan as she goes to a table in the middle of the room, clears a place among the litter of books on it, and puts down the tray. There are piles of books and papers all over the study, all covered in dust.

The MAID *grumbles as she looks round at the general disorder.*

MAID *to herself* : What a filthy mess!

The camera pans after her as she goes out of the door. At the same time, the door of the bedroom opens and RATH *appears. He glances round the room, feels in the pocket of his frock coat, hesitates, and finally goes towards his desk. Medium shot of* RATH *looking at the clutter of books. He picks up a small notebook, leafs through it, and puts it in his coat pocket. He takes his watch from his waistcoat pocket, looks at it, puts it back, and, buttoning the top of his frock coat, goes towards the middle of the room. Pan, then medium shot of* RATH, *facing the camera, as he sits down to breakfast. He pours coffee into a bowl, glances away and whistles. He pours out a small quantity of milk, then looks up and whistles again.*

Close-up of a birdcage hanging by the window in a ray of sunlight. The cage appears to be empty. Cut to RATH, *who puts down the milk jug and with a sly smile, takes a sugar-lump and gets up. Medium close-up of the cage as* RATH, *still whistling, appears beside it and holds up the sugar-lump. Suddenly, he stops whistling and his*

smile fades: he slowly opens the cage and takes out a dead bird, which he strokes sadly. (Still on page 2) He looks at the cage again. A door is heard opening off. Cut to the MAID *coming through the doorway behind* RATH, *carrying the rest of the breakfast — including two boiled eggs — on a tray. Pan after her as she puts down the tray on the table and approaches* RATH, *still standing, mournful and silent, with the bird in his hand. The* MAID *sees the bird and takes it from him.*

MAID *shrugging*: Well! . . . It didn't sing any more, anyway.
She moves out of frame. A new shot, shows her opening the stove and throwing in the dead bird. Cut to RATH, *who gazes at the stove with a horrified expression. Finally the camera pans across as he returns to the table, still holding the sugar-lump intended for the bird. He sits down, looks at the sugar-lump, and then drops it into his bowl of coffee. Sadly, and with bowed head, he stirs his coffee.*

Long shot of a classroom. The teacher is not there. Some boys of about fifteen to sixteen years old are gathered round the window, talking and laughing. In the background, by the master's desk, the form leader is cleaning the blackboard. Medium close-up of the form leader who turns round several times and looks over the top of his spectacles at the group of boys with a furtive and frightened expression. Clean, combed, seeming timid; he is excluded from the rowdy clan formed by his fellow pupils. Medium shot of the group of pupils: they crowd round a youth, LOHMANN, *who is brandishing a postcard-sized photograph, only the back of which is seen.* LOHMANN *holds up the photograph and blows on it. The boys crowd round with interest,* LOHMANN *lets some of the others blow on the photograph. Another pupil pushes forward.*

LOHMANN : Oh . . . get off !
LOHMANN *blows again on the photograph, while another pupil —* GOLDSTAUB *— who is standing beside him, leaves the group and moves out of the picture.*
Medium shot, slightly from above, of one corner of the

master's desk. GOLDSTAUB *approaches cautiously, takes
the schoolmaster's exercise book and a pencil. Insert
close-up of the label on the cover of the book, on which
is written 'PROFESSOR RATH.'* GOLDSTAUB *writes
'UN' in capitals over the name, since the German word
UNRATH means excrement. He also adds a quick
caricature of the schoolmaster. The pencil lead snaps just
as he is finishing the drawing.*

*Long shot of the stairway and landing outside the school-
master's apartment. The door opens and* RATH *emerges,
followed by the* MAID, *who inspects his clothing. He is
wearing a cape and a wide-brimmed hat, and is carrying
a cane and briefcase. He stops on the landing, pats his
pockets as if looking for something, turns round and
back again and finally goes down the stairs. The* MAID
*goes in and shuts the door. A clock begins to strike in
the distance.*

*Close-up on the enormous face of the town-hall clock;
the hands show eight o'clock. After the first note of the
carillon, a white dove flits across the shot. The carillon
turns out to be the tune 'Ueb immer Treu und Redlichkeit' (Be always faithful and honest). Meanwhile the
camera tracks slowly backwards to reveal the whole of the
clock face, including a set of symbolic figures which move
round the clock face in time to the music. The figures
disappear and the clock strikes eight.*

*Long shot of the classroom, still without the school-
master, as the eighth stroke of the clock dies away. A
number of boys are fighting.*

A PUPIL : Let me go. . . . Let me go!

*The form leader is still at the blackboard by the master's
desk.*

ANGST, *the teacher's favourite* : Be quiet! . . . Silence! . . .
Be quiet! Rath's coming.

*His orders have no effect and another pupil knocks into
him. He just manages to avoid falling, and at that
moment,* GOLDSTAUB *bursts into the room.*

GOLDSTAUB : Look out, here comes the old man.

Immediately the boys rush to their places and sit down.

Silence falls. Long shot down the length of a corridor in the school. On the right are windows; on the left, the doors of the classrooms; between them, the pupils' caps and coats hang on stands. There is also a wash basin. In the foreground, seen from behind, the school-master RATH *has taken off his coat and is walking towards the door of his classroom.*
Wide-angle shot of the classroom, seen from the back row: RATH *enters. The pupils, backs to the camera, get up.* RATH *shuts the door and the camera pans as he goes across to the desk. He pauses in stepping up to the rostrum and inspects the class.*

RATH : Sit down!

Noise of the pupils sitting down, while RATH *carefully puts down the three books he has in his hand. Medium shot of* RATH, *sitting down. The camera pans briefly downwards. Keeping his eyes on the class, he extracts a handkerchief from the back pocket of his frock coat, unfolds it carefully, blows his nose noisily, clears his throat, wipes his nose, and returns the handkerchief to a different pocket. After this performance, he turns round the exercise book lying on the desk in front of him, starts to open it, but pauses as his eye falls on the cover. Medium shot of* ANGST, *sitting rigidly at his desk. He looks at* RATH *who is looking at the label of the exercise book. He raises his head slightly and eyes the class over the top of his spectacles. Medium shot of* LOHMANN *and* GOLDSTAUB *sitting at their desks.* GOLD-STAUB *is looking towards the window with an innocent expression;* LOHMANN *is looking at* RATH. *Cut back to* RATH, *who turns his gaze on* ANGST *again. Cut to* ANGST, *grinning stupidly. Cut back to* RATH, *who gets up from his seat.*

RATH *severely* : Angst, come here!

Medium shot of ANGST, *who gets up and hurries nervously to the front. He is seen again in front of* RATH'S *desk.* RATH *hands him the exercise book, together with a rubber.*

RATH : Erase that!

ANGST *bends to pick up the book and the rubber, glancing rapidly at* LOHMANN *and* GOLDSTAUB. RATH *follows his gaze. Cut to* GOLDSTAUB, *seen slightly from above, who grimaces ironically, then suddenly freezes as he notices that* RATH *has his eye on him.* LOHMANN *adjusts his bow tie, then looks at the ceiling and twiddles his thumbs. Return to* RATH *and* ANGST. *The latter rubs out the marks on the book, then hands it and the rubber back to* RATH.

ANGST : Please, Sir. . . .

RATH *bellowing*: Silence! *Waving his hand.* Go and sit down. *Close-up of* GOLDSTAUB, *who smirks with satisfaction, then suddenly assumes a falsely innocent air. Resume on* RATH, *who is now leafing through the exercise book, fiddling with the broken pencil in his right hand. He looks up slowly.*

RATH *sarcastically*: Well, gentlemen. . . . Now we shall see what else you have learnt. *Bending over the book again.* Yesterday we left off at Hamlet, Act Three, Scene One.

RATH's *gaze wanders round the class again and comes to rest. Cut to a pupil —* ERTZUM *— who is buried in a book which he has under his desk. Cut to* RATH, *who narrows his eyes and points a finger at the schoolboy.*

RATH : Ertzum!

Medium shot of ERTZUM, *slightly from above: he rises nervously to his feet, looking embarrassed. Return to* RATH, *who gestures to him to recite.*

RATH : Well . . . out with it!

Quick shot of ERTZUM, *looking more and more embarrassed and visibly searching his memory. Cut back to* RATH, *turning the pencil in his fingers. The camera cuts from one to the other several times.*

RATH *in English*: To be . . . well? To be or not . . . *Cut to* ERTZUM *while* RATH *continues off* : . . . to be!

ERTZUM *repeating hesitantly in English*: To be . . . or not . . . to be . . . that is ze . . . *he pronounces English very badly.*

RATH *waving the pencil* : Stop. No good.

He gets up, steps down from the rostrum and goes

28

towards ERTZUM. *Medium shot of the two of them together.*
RATH : You never pronounce the English article right. *He waves the pencil at him.* Say after me . . . ' The.'
ERTZUM *mispronouncing it* : ' Ze.'
RATH, *in desperation, shakes his head and almost bellows at* ERTZUM, *showering him with saliva.*
RATH : ' The! '
ERTZUM *wiping the spittle from his cheek* : ' Ze.'
In his turn, ERTZUM *showers* RATH *with saliva.* RATH *wipes it from his nose, moves slightly backwards and resumes in a more cautious tone of voice.*
RATH : ' The.'
ERTZUM *copying him* : ' Ze.'
RATH : ' The.'
ERTZUM *concentrating furiously* : ' Ze.'
RATH *with increasing irritation* : Open your mouth. *He puts the pencil between the boy's teeth.* ' The.'
ERTZUM *is embarrassed at being put through this performance in front of the other pupils.*
ERTZUM : ' The! '
RATH *more calmly* : ' The.'
ERTZUM *likewise* : ' The.'
RATH *shrugs his shoulders and snatches the pencil from* ERTZUM'S *mouth.*
RATH : Sit down.
ERTZUM *does as he is told and* RATH, *discouraged, returns to his desk. Group shot of the class, the pupils with their backs to the camera, and* RATH *in the background, returning to his desk.*
RATH : Get out your composition books.
The pupils, seen from behind, do as they are told. RATH *puts down the pencil, cups his chin in his hands and looks at them with a malicious air. Cut to* ERTZUM, *who is gazing expectantly at* RATH.
RATH *off* : Now. . . . *Cut back to him.* Write this down: ' Julius Caesar '. . . . *A pause.* What would have happened if . . . er . . . Mark Anthony . . . *He puts on his glasses* . . . had failed to deliver his oration?

RATH *straightens up and, with an affected gesture of the right hand, stands triumphantly over his pupils. The camera tracks backwards, framing the whole class hard at work. Hands behind his back,* RATH *walks nonchalantly towards the window. Cut to* LOHMANN *and* GOLDSTAUB. RATH *passes in front of them and opens the window wide; through it float strains of the song* 'Aennchen von Thorau,' *sung by a choir of schoolgirls somewhere nearby.* RATH *walks up and down the classroom as the song continues. Group shot of the class, slightly from above: as soon as* RATH'S *back is turned, several pupils copy from their neighbours. One in particular, in the front row turns to* ANGST, *the form leader, who immediately covers his work with a piece of blotting paper.*

Close-up of RATH *leaning against the wall at the back of the classroom. (Still on page 3) He takes off his glasses and wipes them carefully with a handkerchief, meanwhile glancing slyly at the pupils whose backs are towards him. Close-up of* GOLDSTAUB *from behind, seated at his desk. He leans forward and looks over* LOHMANN'S *shoulder. Cut to* RATH, *who notices the movement and puts on his glasses. Return to* GOLDSTAUB, *seen from behind; still in the same position. Cut back to* RATH, *who advances with a determined air. Group shot of* LOHMANN, *holding the photograph, and* GOLDSTAUB. RATH *comes up, leans over and snatches the photograph from* LOHMANN. *He holds it up and looks at it in horror, then looks sternly from one pupil to the other. Suddenly, he turns round, still holding the photograph. Pan after him as he goes to the window, and shuts it with a bang. The sound of the girls' choir is muted.* RATH *hurries back to his desk.*

Medium shot of RATH *sitting down and looking severely at* LOHMANN.

RATH : Get up!

Cut to LOHMANN, *who gets up uneasily. Resume on* RATH *who examines the confiscated photograph closely and inserts it carefully in a small note-book. He then addresses*

30

Lohmann, *his arm outstretched.*

Rath : Sit down!

Cut to Lohmann, *who does as he is told, and cut back to* Rath, *who waves the notebook, menacingly in the air.*

Rath : This will be discussed later.

He stuffs the notebook in the inside pocket of his jacket and fumbles as he fastens the top button of his coat. He then takes out his handkerchief and blows his nose noisily as before. While he is doing this, the camera cuts to Lohmann, *who is looking at* Angst. *Sound of* Rath *blowing his nose, off. Shot of* Angst *smirking with satisfaction. He dips his pen in the inkwell and starts to write. Fade out.*

Fade in : Lohmann *and* Ertzum *are crouching in front of the school entrance. They are clearly hiding, and remain unnoticed as the other pupils pass in front of them. The scene is shot from the eye-level of the two boys, so that only the legs of the other pupils and the briefcases in their hands are visible. After a moment,* Rath *walks past with measured tread, followed immediately by* Angst. Ertzum *sticks his foot out and trips up* Angst. Angst *falls flat on the ground, dropping a pile of books in the process, while* Ertzum *and* Lohmann *disappear. Medium close-up from above of* Angst *sprawled on the ground. He lifts his head, looking dazed.* Rath, *in medium close-up from below, has turned round on hearing the noise of* Angst's *fall and is looking back at him. Shot of* Angst *from above with dishevelled hair and his cap on crooked.* Rath *stares at the ground in surprise.* Angst, *shot from above, follows* Rath's *gaze and swallows uneasily. Close-up of the books strewn on the ground. Pan across some exercise books from which have fallen photographs of* Lola. *Fade out.*

Fade in : The entrance hall in Rath's *apartment, the dismayed* Angst *is standing in front of the study door, clutching his books.* Rath *hangs up his cane, then takes off his hat and coat and hangs them up. He then picks up a book and a file of papers from the side table, and he points at the study door.*

RATH *severely* : Inside!

ANGST *opens the door and enters the study, followed by* RATH. *Inside* RATH'S *study,* ANGST *is seen entering, followed by* RATH. RATH *goes to the table, takes a chair, moves it near to an armchair and sits down in the latter. He then turns and beckons peremptorily off shot.*

RATH : Come over here!

ANGST *is seen still standing by the door, twisting his cap in his hands.*

He advances nervously across the room. Medium shot of the two of them, as RATH *relieves him of his books and puts them on the table. He then indicates the empty chair by his side.*

RATH : Sit down!

ANGST *sits down and looks at the floor. Close-up of the two of them.*

RATH *bitterly* : You as well! *Shaking his head.* My form leader!

ANGST *plaintively* : Please, sir. . . .

RATH *interrupting*: Be quiet! *A pause.* RATH *studies his pupil.* Aren't you ashamed of yourself?

ANGST : But, Sir, I . . .

RATH *interrupting* : Silence! Look at me. ANGST *looks up.* RATH *continues severely.* Where did you get those photographs?

ANGST *miserably* : I don't know. . . .

RATH : You're lying! Where did you get them?

ANGST *hesitantly* : Someone must have planted them on me.

RATH *dubiously*: Really? *He leans closer to* ANGST *and raises his left eyebrow.* You think I'm going to believe that?

ANGST *finally bursting into tears* : They all hate me . . because I won't go with them in the evenings.

RATH *seizing him by the lapels*: Where won't you go with them?

ANGST : The others . . .

RATH : Come on, the truth now.

ANGST *hesitantly* : Every night they all go to THE BLUE ANGEL. . . . There are females!

Rath *beside himself* : Where?
Angst : At THE BLUE ANGEL.
Rath *staring at* Angst *in astonishment and letting him go:*
At THE BLUE ANGEL?...
Without taking his eyes from Angst, *he falls back in his chair. After a pause, he leans in front of his chastened pupil and takes the notebook from the table. He opens it, takes out the photograph confiscated from* Lohmann, *and examines it closely, addressing* Angst *as he does so. (Still on page 4)*
Rath : Off you go. We'll see about this later.
From his chair, Rath *watches* Angst *shuffle towards the door.* Angst *bows and goes out.*
Close-up of Rath, *full face. He looks closely at the photograph, then takes from his pocket the other two photographs confiscated from* Angst. *He fans out the three photographs. After a moment or two, he glances towards the door to reassure himself and then studies the photographs again. He blows on the middle one, as* Lohmann *and the other pupils did earlier. He glances round again, first at the window, then the door. He blows on the photograph, a little harder.*
Close-up of the three photographs in Rath's *hand. (Still on page 4) They represent LOLA-LOLA. In the middle photograph, her skirt is made of pieces of feathers which lift when* Rath *blows on them, revealing her thighs.* Rath *blows again and again. The first notes of a popular tune are heard off.*
A night-club is seen in medium shot, shot slightly from below. Lola *stands in the centre of the stage of* THE BLUE ANGEL. *She is swinging in time to the music, while behind her several other girls, all on the fat side, are sitting drinking beer. The décor, only party visible, is rather crude and consists of a sun throwing out long rays with cardboard clouds floating in front of it.* Lola *is dressed in a close-fitting black costume covered in sequins and has a brightly-coloured ribbon in her hair. Hands on her hips, she gazes at the audience with a disinterested and contemptuous look. (Still on page 21)*

Medium shot of a cardboard 'angel' which forms part of the décor: he has movable wings and his expression is more fatuous than angelic.

In long shot in the foreground, LOLA stands with her legs apart, her stockings and suspenders well displayed; behind her, the other women drink their beer. Other parts of the décor are now visible, including a sailing boat, fishing nets and anchors.

Group shot of the stage with the first few rows of the audience seen from the back in the foreground. Gauze curtains hang to right and left of the stage; cardboard clouds and angels swing to and fro, crudely suspended from the flies.

A WAITER *off, very loud* : Pig's knuckles and sauerkraut . . . and one beer!

LOLA *singing* :

Ich bin die fesche Lola	(My name is naughty Lola
Der Liebling der Saison	The fav'rite of the gang
Ich hab ein Pianola	I have a pianola
Zu Haus, in mein Salon	At home with lots of tang
Ich bin die fesche Lola	My name is naughty Lola
Mich liebt ein jeder Mann	The men all go for me
Doch an mein Pianola	But for my pianola
Da lass ich keinen dran	That's only there to see
Doch will mich wer	If you wish to play it
begleiten	You in this cabaret
Hier unten aus dem Saal	I'll bang you on the shins
Dem hau ich in die Seiten	And make you rue the day)
Und tret ihm auf's Pedal	

LOLA turns and goes nonchalantly back to her place with the other girls; she sits down, re-arranging her hair. There is a satisfied murmur from the audience. The waiters can also be heard shouting their orders: 'Beer! . . . Sausage! . . .' A medium shot, slightly from below, shows LOLA seated on the stage. She takes a glass of beer from her neighbour, drinks, and hands it back.

MAN'S VOICE *off* : Three more beers.

Long shot of the stage as LOLA gets up, wiping her mouth with the end of her hair-ribbon. She advances once again to the centre of the stage and continues to sing in the same blasé manner as before.

Long shot, slightly angled, of an ill-lit alley-way; it is night time. Recognisable by his cape, RATH *hurries along. He is wearing the same hat as before and brandishing his cane. The camera tracks, then pans to follow him as he goes along.*

RATH *stops under a street lamp, as if uncertain of his way, and looks around in some embarrassment. He hesitates. In a doorway on the other side of the street, a prostitute waits for a client, smoking a cigarette.*

The camera tracks with RATH *and pans with him as he crosses the street; he stops very briefly, turns up his collar and hurries off. The prostitute bursts out laughing.*

Long shot of the stage of THE BLUE ANGEL : *the scenery is being changed. A stage-hand stands in the middle of the platform and looks up. The band begins to play* 'Ach! Du lieber Augustin,' *and at the same time, there are impatient shouts from the audience. A middle-aged woman,* GUSTE, *gets up from her place on the stage, comes towards the footlights and begins to sing.*

LOLA'S *dressing room* : LOLA *is seated at her dressing table, facing the camera. She is powdering her face, watched intently by the seated* LOHMANN *and the standing* GOLDSTAUB *and* ERTZUM. *They are wearing their school caps and smoking.*

LOLA *hands* GOLDSTAUB *her powder-puff and takes* LOHMANN'S *cigarette from his mouth; she draws on it and then gives it back to him.*

LOHMANN, ERTZUM *and* GOLDSTAUB *look on, fascinated, as* LOLA *straightens her wig. (Still on page 21)*

A long shot of the stage shows GUSTE *still singing. She finishes her song and is greeted by whistles from the audience.*

Outside in the ill-lit street, RATH, *shot from above, walks past houses with overhanging walls. As he passes a lamp-post, a ship's siren echoes in the night. A policeman, leaning against a poster of '* LOLA-LOLA *' stuck on the wall, turns to watch* RATH *as he disappears into the distance.*

Inside THE BLUE ANGEL: *a long shot of the stage with scenery representing a fountain. On the left is a bentwood chair, to the right a spotlight. The ' girls' are still seated on the stage, drinking their beer. The band strikes up, and* LOLA *appears to general applause, wearing a blonde wig topped by a small three-cornered hat and a crinoline dress with transparent skirts which displays her thighs and legs.* LOLA *bows to the audience with a smile and sways provocatively in time to the music, her hands behind her back.*

LOLA *singing*: Frühling kommt, der Sperling piept
Duft aus Blüten Kelchen
(Spring is here, sparrows chirp
Fragrant blossoms flower)

As she sings, LOLA *flutters her hands and cups one of them to her ear as if listening. The clarinet responds with an imitation of the sparrow. The audience laughs. In a group shot,* ERTZUM, LOHMANN *and* GOLDSTAUB *are seen leaning against the bar, drinking and smoking cigarettes. All three are gazing at the stage in fascination. A little further back, the* PROPRIETOR *is seen behind the bar, close to the till.*

LOLA *off*: Bin in einen Mann verliebt
Und weiss nicht in welchen
Ob er Geld hat ist mir gleich
Denn mich macht die Liebe reich
(Love someone who is a man
But can't tell who is he
I don't care if he's well off
Love alone enriches me)

GOLDSTAUB *moves out of frame. Cut to* LOLA, *shot slightly from below, with her arms outstretched, as if in invitation to the schoolboy.*

LOLA : Kinder, heut abend, da such ich mir was aus
Einen Mann, einen richtigen Mann *(Still on page 22)*
(Children, tonight, I look for someone real

36

A he-man, the right kind for me)
*One of the girls goes over to the spotlight and turns it
on the audience.*
LOLA *still singing, moving towards the spotlight* :
Kinder, die Jungs häng mir schon zum Hals heraus
Einen Mann, einen richtigen Mann
(Children, the young are a pain in the neck !
The real man, the right kind for me)
*She turns round: the crinoline only covers one side of
her, the other reveals black-stockinged legs and lacy
briefs. There are hurrahs from the audience. She throws
back her head, smiles, and continues with her song.*
LOLA *singing* :
Einen Mann dem das Feuer aus den Augen glüht
Einen Mann dem das Feuer aus den Augen sprüht
(One whose heart still glows with thoughts of love
One whose eyes shoot out passionate fire)
Cut to the glass door of THE BLUE ANGEL. *The
camera is on the inside; on the outside,* RATH *is seen in
close-up. He peers through the misted window, then opens
the door.*
Another shot shows RATH *coming hesitantly into the
club. In the background,* LOLA *continues her song.*
RATH'S *glasses become misted; the fishing nets that hang
in the entrance and in the aisles bar his way.*
LOLA *off* : Kurz einen Mann der noch lieben will und kann
Einen Mann, einen richtigen Mann
(In short, one who's willing to love and be held
The real thing, and not a fraud)
Cut to the bar. ERTZUM *has just seen* RATH *and hastily
removes his cap, pushes against* LOHMANN *and disappears.
Taken aback,* LOHMANN *throws away his cigarette and
follows* ERTZUM. *Near them a* CLOWN *observes the
audience. Pan from his gaze past several provocative
posters of* LOLA *towards* RATH, *who is seen picking his
way through the nets down the side of the club. Close-up
of* RATH *caught in a net as in a gigantic spider's web.
A raucous sound from the clarinet seems to mock his
predicament.*

37

LOLA *still singing off* : Männer gibt es dünn und dick
Gross und klein und kräftig
Andere wieder schön und schick
schüchtern oder heftig
Wie er aussieht mir egal
Irgend einen trifft die Wahl
(Men there are, thin and thick
Large and small and hefty
Others may be nice and quick
Bashful or aggressive
How he looks means nought to me
Someone here will fill the bill)

Medium close-up of LOLA, *smiling, as she stops singing and goes towards the spotlight. Taking the place of the other girl, who goes and sits down beside* GUSTE, *she directs the beam of light on the audience, who shout invitations at her.*

MAN IN THE AUDIENCE *off* : Hey! Look over here! . . . Over here!

Others follow suit with cries of ' Oh me, me! ' — ' Over here, darling! ' — ' This way, Lola! Here's the cash.'
Close-up of RATH, *who turns round suddenly as the beam hits him. He blinks in confusion, the light reflecting off his spectacles.*

LOLA *singing off*: Kinder, heut abend, da such ich mir was aus
Rapid pan to her standing by the spotlight.
Cut back to RATH, *furious and bewildered, looking wildly from the stage to the audience and back again. There are shouts and mocking laughter off, while* LOLA *continues relentlessly with her song.*

LOLA *off* : Einen Mann, einen richtigen Mann
Medium close-up as she leans on the spotlight.

LOLA *off*: Kinder, die Jungs häng mir schon zum Hals heraus
Resume on RATH, *in medium close-up, gazing wide-eyed at the stage. Suddenly he turns and stares in the direction of the bar.*

LOLA *off* : Einen Mann, einen richtigen Mann

The camera shows RATH'S *view of the bar. In front of it,* GOLDSTAUB *stands nonchalantly watching the show. Behind the bar near the till stands the* PROPRIETOR *of* THE BLUE ANGEL, *a large bulky man who is listening with evident satisfaction to the reactions of the audience.* GOLDSTAUB *suddenly catches sight of* RATH, *panics, snatches off his cap, and runs off towards the wings.*

LOLA *off* : Einen Mann dem das Feuer aus den Augen glüht
RATH, *shot from above, stands in the midst of the seated audience, still in the glare of the spotlight. The sight of* GOLDSTAUB *making off galvanises him into action. He waves his cane and struggles to find a way through the crowd.*

RATH : Stop! . . . Stop! . . . Stay where you are!

LOLA *off, simultaneously with* RATH : Einen Mann dem das Feuer aus den Augen sprüht
Cut to GOLDSTAUB, *disappearing backstage. There are shouts and laughter from the audience drowning* LOLA'S *song.*

In medium shot, RATH *rushes towards the door which leads backstage, and bumps into the* CLOWN, *who is standing in his way. After a moment's deliberation, the* CLOWN *lets him through and closes the door behind him. The camera following* RATH *backstage, pans across a* RATH *looks around him in confusion. In the background on the stage,* LOLA *invites the audience to sing with her in* THE BLUE ANGEL.

LOLA : Come on, all together, now! *They all sing.*

RATH, *seen from behind, strides up to a door backstage and flings it open, revealing several of the chorus girls in various states of undress. He looks round in embarrassment and goes out again, shutting the door.*

RATH *now finds himself in* LOLA'S *dressing room, which he examines. There are two doors, one leading to the dressing rooms of the other performers, the other giving directly onto the wings. A spiral staircase leads up to* LOLA'S *bedroom. The stage door opens and the* CLOWN *appears. A girl passes by behind him. He watches* RATH *wall covered with mirrors, posters and photographs.*

39

*for a moment and then stands motionless. The audience
is heard in the background, singing with* LOLA.

RATH *advances across the room until he is standing by
a screen in front of* LOLA's *dressing table. He listens.
Applause is heard off, marking the end of* LOLA's *act,
and he immediately hurries over to the staircase and
goes up it out of sight. Cut to* GOLDSTAUB, *shot from
above, crouching behind the screen and reflected in two
mirrors. Cut to medium close-up of the* CLOWN, *who
catches sight of* GOLDSTAUB *and comes back into the
room.*

*Medium shot of the band, seen from above; the pianist
drinks from a glass of beer and then strikes up an oriental
melody, followed by the trumpet and the saxophone. A
large fountain is painted on the backdrop behind them.
A very fat girl comes onto the stage in medium close-up;
she sways in time to the music, rolling her eyes.*

Pan on LOLA's *entrance into her dressing room. She
goes to the table, takes off her hat and, suddenly hearing
a strange noise, turns towards the staircase leading up to
her bedroom.*

LOLA *sharply* : What are you doing in my bedroom?

Very slowly, RATH *comes down the stairs with* LOLA
watching. (Still on page 23)

RATH *brandishing his cane* : So you're Lola-Lola?

Somewhat surprised, but also reassured by RATH's
general appearance, LOLA *goes to her table, takes off
her wig and starts to brush her hair.*

LOLA : You're from the police?

RATH : Indeed not, madam! I am . . . *He puffs out his chest.*
. . . Doctor Immanuel Rath, schoolmaster of this town.

Shot of LOLA *and* RATH *both together.* LOLA *examines*
RATH *with curiosity. She smiles ironically, then bends
down at her dressing table and continues brushing her
hair.*

LOLA *contemptuously* : In that case you might at least take
off your hat. . . .

Close-up of RATH, *who jumps backwards in embarrassment and hastily removes his hat. (Still on page 23) A*

40

*man and a woman are heard quarrelling violently off.
Their voices become suddenly louder as the door to the
other dressing room opens to reveal the* CLOWN. *He shuts
the door and the voices fade. Cut to* LOLA *applying lipstick. Return to the* CLOWN *passing in front of* RATH,
*who looks at him uneasily. He opens the stage door and
the room is filled with oriental music. The* CLOWN *eyes*
RATH *without any expression and then disappears through
the door, shutting it behind him.* RATH *turns towards*
LOLA. *A new shot shows them facing one another.*

LOLA *putting on her lipstick*: What are you doing here, then?

RATH *pompously*: I am here in an official capacity. *He points
at* LOLA. You are corrupting my pupils!

LOLA: Really! You think I run a kindergarten?

Pan after LOLA *as she rises and goes behind the screen,
undoing the back of her skirt. She sees* GOLDSTAUB. *Cut
to a high shot of* GOLDSTAUB, *crouched by the mirror.
Return to* LOLA, *who smiles at him and moves the screen
slightly to hide him better. She then removes her skirt
and drapes it over the screen. Medium close-up on* RATH,
*who has been following her movements closely. In
medium shot,* LOLA *comes out from behind the screen
wearing the upper half of her costume and a petticoat.
She puts one foot up on the chair and takes off her
shoe, showing her thighs in the process. Medium close-up
of* RATH *watching her with interest. He suddenly pulls
himself together and turns his head away, still watching*
LOLA, *however, out of the corner of his eye. Cut back to*
LOLA, *who takes off her stockings, smiling at* RATH *as
she does so. Then she throws the stocking she has just
taken off, over her shoulder, and addresses him.*

LOLA: Now, you don't say anything any more.

Cut to RATH, *now staring openly at* LOLA. *He turns,
and, with as much dignity as he can muster, he goes
towards the door, which suddenly opens. The music
marking the end of the act onstage is heard and the girls
troop through, bumping into* RATH *and eyeing him
curiously. Finding him blocking her way, one of the girls
complains.*

GIRL : For god's sake! . . . You're obstructing the traffic.

After the girls comes the CLOWN, *who pushes* RATH *back into the room and shuts the door. On the other side of the room by the door, two girls are sneering at* RATH.

GIRL : Just look what's crawled in!

They go out, shutting the door.

Return to LOLA, *who is watching* RATH *and playing with her stocking.*

RATH *off* : I really can't stay here . . . *Shot of him by the door* . . . I am compromising you.

LOLA moves into the shot until she is standing face to face with RATH. *He draws back a little.*

LOLA *smiling* : If you're . . . very good . . . *She speaks very slowly* . . . you can stay.

With a mischievous air, she gently takes RATH'S *hat from him and puts it on the table. Then she passes in front of* RATH, *brushing against him, and the camera pans after her as she goes up the staircase.* RATH *stands mopping his brow, while in the background* LOLA'S *legs are still visible at the top of the staircase. A pair of briefs slides down her legs.*

LOLA *partly off* : Look out, below . . . I'm taking everything off now!

Taking off her briefs, she throws them down from the top of the stairs, and they land on RATH'S *shoulder. He takes the garment and tries unsuccessfully to fold it. At this moment,* GUSTE *comes in through the stage door, looks at* RATH *dubiously, and takes the briefs from him.*

GUSTE *wagging a finger at him* : You! You! I don't want to hear any complaints from you.

Briefs in hand, she moves away from RATH, *leaving him speechless. Music is heard in the club.* GUSTE, *in front of the other door, looks alternately from* RATH *to the briefs, then throws the garment under the screen. More music from the club. A high shot of* GOLDSTAUB *catching the briefs behind the screen. Return to* RATH *who looks nervously in the direction of the stage. He has obviously not seen* GOLDSTAUB. GUSTE *glances at* RATH *once more and goes out, shutting the door. Return to* RATH, *who looks around him and particularly at the staircase, while music, stage noises and laughter are heard off. RATH leans wearily on LOLA's dressing table and sits down heavily. He takes off his glasses, passes a hand across his eyes, gets out his handkerchief and starts to clean his glasses. He squints at the stage door which must be open, judging by the noise. The camera pans as an animal trainer goes past RATH, leading a bear on its hind legs. In passing, the trainer glances at RATH, who shrinks in his chair in alarm. The trainer goes out of the other door, followed by the bear. Cut back to RATH gazing after them in stupefaction, still holding his handkerchief and glasses.*

In her bedroom, LOLA in her black underwear climbs onto a pile of suitcases to reach a hatbox on top of a cupboard. A suitcase slips and falls noisily.

In the dressing room below, RATH hears the noise and looks upwards. High shot of GOLDSTAUB, seen crawling out from his hiding place. He puts LOLA's briefs in the back pocket of RATH's frock coat, without the latter noticing. Cut to RATH, who looks around himself in increasing bewilderment.

Up in her bedroom, LOLA casually gets ready to go down. LOLA comes down the staircase and smiles at RATH, sitting in the chair. Pan as she goes towards him, takes him by the shoulders and turns him round in his chair.

LOLA : Do you like me better like this, then?

She passes in front of RATH, who turns, moving out of frame. Close-up on GOLDSTAUB, peering out from behind the screen. Medium shot of LOLA standing by the piano; she puts on a short skirt. The bell calling her onstage rings.

Close-up on RATH, who puts on his spectacles and looks at LOLA while the bell rings again. He raises his head, and LOLA is seen fastening her skirt.

LOLA : They seem to be in a hurry out there !

She leans across the piano, striking several keys as she does so, and reaches for her hat. Cut to RATH observing

LOLA *with astonishment and interest. Return to* LOLA, *who puts on the hat, straightens her skirt and smiles at* RATH. RATH *turns away and gets up. Medium shot of* LOLA *adjusting bonnet.*

RATH *searching around him* : I wonder where I put my hat. *The door opens behind* RATH *to admit* KIEPERT, *the manager of the troupe, followed by his assembled artistes.*

A WOMAN *off* : I won't drink any more!

KIEPERT *bellowing* : You'll just have to soak, ladies. You think I give a damn about art? Rubbish! And if you don't want to guzzle, you can get out!

ANOTHER WOMAN : About the commission . . .

KIEPERT *interrupting her* : Shut up! Once and for all, quiet! *He turns and sees* LOLA *and* RATH. How did this joker happen to be here?

LOLA : He's only the kids' teacher.

KIEPERT *looks at* LOLA, *takes off and puts on his false moustache, and addresses* RATH *obsequiously.*

KIEPERT : Professor. . . .

RATH *bowing in confirmation* : At the university. KIEPERT *raises his top hat.* Doctor Immanuel Rath.

KIEPERT : Then we're bound to understand each other.

RATH : What do you mean?

KIEPERT *pointing at himself* : Art and . . . *indicating* RATH : Science. *He approaches Rath who draws back slowly.* Allow me to introduce myself! Kiepert, manager and conjurer. *The door closes behind him, as he addresses* LOLA, *who is combing her hair.* Why wasn't I called immediately? *To* RATH, *with an ingratiating bow.* I am delighted to be able to welcome in our midst one of the most eminent personalities of this town.

Pan to RATH, *who draws back slowly, shaking his head.*

RATH : I have come . . .

KIEPERT : I know, because you feel at home here.

RATH *retreating further* : No. I have come . . .

KIEPERT : Indeed, I can see that you have. And I am delighted. . . .

He glares at LOLA, *out of frame. As* RATH *comes back towards him, pan with* KIEPERT *as he strides across to*

44

LOLA. LOLA *is doing her hair in front of the mirror.*
KIEPERT *appears, putting on his top hat.*
KIEPERT *furious*: I said why wasn't I called? Am I the manager or aren't I?
LOLA *taking her hands away from her head*: You're a stupid old bit of beef.
KIEPERT *is speechless. The bell rings again.*
KIEPERT *with a furious gesture*: Get out there! Go and do your number!
LOLA, *hands behind her back, looks contemptuously at the two men. She addresses* KIEPERT.
LOLA *full of sarcasm*: Don't overdo it, will you?
As she moves out of frame, cut to RATH, *who has been watching the dispute indignantly. In medium shot,* LOLA *opens the stage door, adjusts her costume, and goes out with a smile of contempt. From a close-up of* RATH, *the camera tracks backwards to show him retreating as* KIEPERT *comes towards him again.*
KIEPERT *facing camera*: Fascinating woman! . . . *He strokes his moustache. A pause.* Herr Professor, I really must congratulate you on your impeccable taste.
RATH *fleeing behind the screen*: I beg your pardon?
KIEPERT *still advancing on* RATH: Come, come, don't get excited. We can talk man to man.
Cut to the CLOWN *entering from the stage door. Music filters through from the club.*
KIEPERT *off*: I can fix it up for you. . . . The girl is very . . .
In medium shot, RATH *and* KIEPERT *face each other.*
KIEPERT *insistently*: . . . is very . . .
RATH *raising an indignant finger*: I have come about my pupils.
KIEPERT: Your pupils?
RATH *furious*: You've been harbouring my pupils!
KIEPERT: Me?
RATH: Yes!
KIEPERT: But we only let in . . .
RATH *beside himself with rage and waving his arms frantically*: Miserable liar!
LOLA *begins to sing off.*

45

KIEPERT: Liar?

RATH *takes a step backwards.* GOLDSTAUB, *shot from above, cries out in pain, appears from behind the screen and rushes past* RATH. *The screen falls over.*

RATH: What's this? Stop! . . . Come here, you rascal! Stop! . . . Stop!

RATH *rushes forward, waving his cane. Rapid pan to follow him, as he runs to the door, knocks into the* CLOWN, *and goes out.*

A high-angle shot of the street shows the entrance to THE BLUE ANGEL. *The walls of the night-club are covered with posters of* LOLA. RATH *comes suddenly from the club, hesitates and looks around him. Applause is heard off, as* LOLA *finishes her song.*

RATH *waving his cane*: Stop! . . . Stop! . . . Stop!

He rushes off down the street. Fade out.

Inside the school dormitory, ANGST *is lying in bed in the darkness. Hearing a curious noise, he sits up nervously in bed. Two figures appear silhouetted against the wall. Ghostly hands rear threateningly over him. Before he can react, the two forms fling themselves upon him, raining blows. He cries out shrilly.*

RATH *is seen going up the staircase outside his apartment. He reaches the landing, turns, then opens the door of his apartment. Fade out.*

In his bedroom, RATH *sits with a glazed look, his hair dishevelled, exhausted. He passes a hand across his brow, then feels in his pocket after a moment; he draws out* LOLA'S *briefs, wipes his forehead with them as if they were his handkerchief, and looks at them again. Suddenly, aware of them, he lets them fall and slumps in his chair.*

A high shot over the roofs of the town.

RATH *comes out of his study into the hall of his apartment. He searches in his pockets and picks up his coat. The* MAID *hurries to help him. He thanks her with a dignified wave of the hand and picks up his briefcase and cane, but suddenly realises that his hat is not in its accustomed position on the hatstand.*

MAID, *hands on hips*: Where have you left your hat this time?

Ignoring her question, RATH still searches on the hall table and the hatstand, which he examines for some time. He starts, as if suddenly remembering where the hat is, disappears into his room and comes out again rapidly, wearing a top hat. Ignoring the MAID, he strides out of the apartment. A new shot shows him descending the staircase. The MAID, seen from below, watches him in surprise from the landing.

A series of shots dissolve into one another showing the figures on the town clock, the clock face, and the hands indicating eight o'clock as in a previous sequence.

Inside RATH's classroom, a long shot from the rostrum shows the pupils sitting quietly at their desks. They turn their heads at the sound of the door opening and stand up. Back view of RATH sitting down at his desk; in the background, the pupils stand. He gestures at them wearily.

RATH : All right. Sit down, please.

The pupils sit down. LOHMANN and GOLDSTAUB look at each other, surprised, while RATH, following his customary ritual, takes out his handkerchief. Medium close-up on RATH from the front; he blows his nose, wipes it, puts the handkerchief back in his pocket and opens the exercise book, which he leafs through, looking over the top of his glasses in the direction of ANGST. Medium close-up of ANGST sitting rigidly at his desk, avoiding the schoolmaster's gaze. Return to RATH, who continues to leaf through the book, while his eyes travel across the class. GOLDSTAUB, in medium close-up, looks across at the window with an air of false preoccupation. Cut back to RATH. Still leafing through the book, he looks down the middle row of the class. Medium shot of ERTZUM, who stares back insolently, but finally drops his eyes and twiddles his thumbs. RATH turns over a few more pages, looking at ANGST. ANGST sits gaping with an air of increasing desperation. RATH, totally unmoved, undoes the top button of his coat, takes out his notebook and

47

writes in it, still looking at ANGST. *Cut to* GOLDSTAUB; *he looks surprised, then throws a malicious glance at* ANGST. RATH, *frowning, finishes writing, his eyes still fixed on* ANGST. ANGST, *in medium close-up, swallows uneasily. Fade out.*

A long shot from above shows the street taken by RATH *the previous evening. It is night. A cat sits in the road, miaowing. As* RATH *comes into view, the cat flees to the safety of a window sill. Under the streetlamp* RATH *pauses to check his direction and moves off again. His shadow looms across the wall. The cat miaows.*

A siren is heard. RATH *stops in another street under a streetlamp, walks on, turns back, passes another lamp, and turns back again, his shadow lengthening in the lamplight.*

In her dressing room, LOLA *is seated, facing the camera, at her dressing table. One one side of her stands* ERTZUM, *wearing his school cap; on the other* LOHMANN, *smoking a cigarette.*

LOLA : Oh ! . . . And he said nothing at all ?

ERTZUM : Of course not. He's afraid of us.

LOHMANN *leaning close and speaking in English in* LOLA'S *ear* : I love you.

LOLA : Cut the English nonsense, sweetie.

> LOHMANN *draws back while* LOLA *wipes her hands on a cloth.*

ERTZUM : Now you've upset him.

LOLA : Bah ! He'll recover.

> LOHMANN *goes and opens the stage door. Music and laughter are heard.* KIEPERT, *the manager of the troupe, comes down the steps from the stage in a fury, brandishing a rabbit and shoving the* CLOWN.

KIEPERT *to the* CLOWN : You stupid old fool, you've messed up the whole number ! I ask for a fish so you come out with a rabbit. *He enters the dressing room.* Ah ! The young students. Back again already ?

> LOHMANN *fishes a banknote out of his pocket and holds it out to* KIEPERT, *who examines it attentively.*

KIEPERT *taking the note and putting it away* : One more time

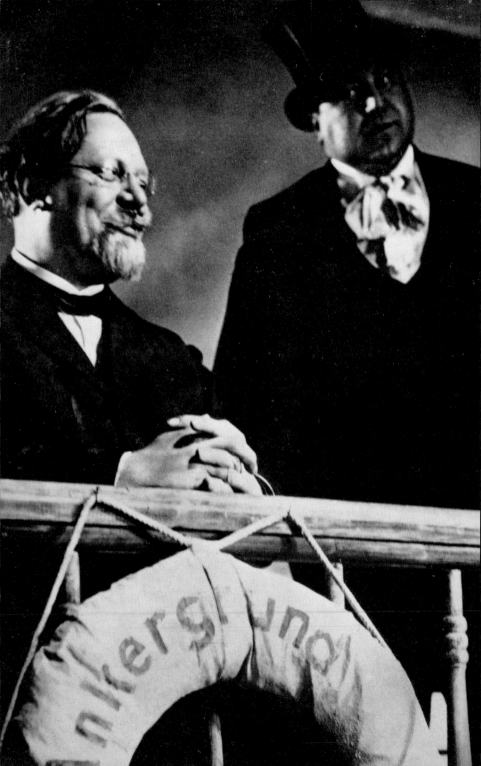

I'll let you in . . . But watch out. You'll make me lose my licence.

Cut to the dressing room window seen from the outside. GOLDSTAUB *leans out, suddenly looks away in alarm and hurriedly shuts the window. In medium shot, inside the dressing room,* GOLDSTAUB *rushes towards* ERTZUM *and* LOHMANN.

GOLDSTAUB : He's coming!

ERTZUM *flinging himself at* GOLDSTAUB : Who?

GOLDSTAUB *tearing off his school cap* : Unrath!

ERTZUM *snatches off his cap and rushes towards the door where* KIEPERT *is standing.*

KIEPERT *holding them back* : No, no! No, no! Not through the hall, gentlemen, if you please. Into the cellar.

The camera pans on LOHMANN, ERTZUM *and* GOLD-STAUB *as they hurry to the trap door leading down into the cellar, fling it open and disappear.*

RATH *arrives at the club entrance with a small parcel in his hand. (Still on page 24) Music and singing off.*

Pan on RATH *walking down a corridor backstage. As he passes a poster of ' LOLA-LOLA,' his top hat knocks against a lamp bracket sticking out from the wall. He straightens his hat. Medium shot outside* LOLA'S *dressing-room; on the left, the* CLOWN. KIEPERT *is standing by* LOLA'S *door holding his rabbit. On seeing* RATH, *he raises his top hat.*

KIEPERT : 'Evening, Professor. This *is* a surprise.

RATH *also raises his hat, then turns towards the* CLOWN.

KIEPERT *motions* RATH *into the dressing room.* RATH *starts forward; but before he finally enters the room, he looks once more at the* CLOWN, *who remains silent. Music and singing are heard off.*

Inside her dressing room, LOLA *is arranging her costume in front of her mirror. She turns and smiles. In a reverse shot,* RATH *stands in the doorway; behind him,* KIEPERT *and the* CLOWN.

LOLA *off* : You can always come straight in, Herr Professor. You're very welcome here.

With great ceremony, RATH *removes his top hat, gives*

a little bow, shuts the door and turns towards LOLA. *He gazes at her.*

LOLA *off* : I knew you would come back.

Shot of LOLA *removing the ribbon from her hair.*

LOLA *smiling* : They all come back to see me!

LOLA *lifts up her skirt, which is open at the front, and her petticoat, as* RATH *enters the picture, carrying his parcel. A new shot shows the pair of them face to face.*

RATH : Madam . . . in my haste . . . yesterday evening . . . I seem to have taken . . . instead of my hat . . . this . . . this . . . *he hesitates* . . . garment.

LOLA *takes the parcel, opens it and finds her briefs inside. Letting the underclothing slip through her fingers, she smiles at* RATH *with her head on one side.*

LOLA *caressingly* : Ah, I see. . . . And you didn't come because of me at all?

She drops the briefs, takes RATH'S *hat and cane and puts them down behind her. Sudden music from inside the club indicates that the stage door has been opened.* RATH *stands still, highly embarrassed.* LOLA *pushes a chair towards him as he turns to look in the direction of the door. Cut to the* CLOWN *who comes into the room holding a rabbit. In a group shot,* LOLA *helps* RATH *off with his coat, while the* CLOWN *advances in the foreground, his back to the camera.* RATH *continues to stare at this silent witness, while* LOLA *goes and hangs up* RATH'S *coat. A new shot shows the* CLOWN *looking at* RATH *with a sad and weary expression before going out of the door. Cut to a shot of the dressing table:* LOLA *sits* RATH *down in the chair close beside her.*

Long shot of the stage, slightly from below: GUSTE *is singing, swaying her hips and holding a glass of beer. The other chorus girls are visible in the background.*

GUSTE *singing* : And if you all go together . . . forwards . . . backwards . . . down . . . up . . . from right to left.

She invites the other girls and the audience to sing, which they do. There is loud music and applause.

In a long shot across the dressing room, LOLA, *standing by the door with her hands on her hips, looks at* RATH *slowly up and down. The music and applause can be heard in the background.* LOLA *glances outside the dressing room, then smiles and shuts the door, cutting off the noise.*

In medium shot in front of the dressing table, LOLA *sits down beside* RATH, *who is fiddling with his bow tie and watching her. She hands him the box of mascara.*

LOLA : Here, hold that a moment.

RATH *holds the box open in front of him while* LOLA *spits in it. She then rubs a small brush in it, which she applies to her eyelashes.*

LOLA : I have beautiful eyes . . . don't you think? RATH *turns away as* LOLA *leans towards him.* They're not beautiful, then?

RATH *embarrassed* : Oh yes . . . yes. . . . They're very . . . very beautiful.

Medium close-up from above on the trap door leading to the cellar; it lifts gently. ERTZUM, GOLDSTAUB *and* LOHMANN *watch* LOLA *and their schoolmaster in great amusement. Cut back to the pair of them, facing the camera.*

LOLA : So you're not here in an official capacity today?

She smiles at RATH'S *embarrassment. He replies after a long pause.*

RATH *embarrassed* : I am afraid I did not behave very properly yesterday.

LOLA *takes the mascara from him, puts it down and picks up a packet of cigarettes.*

LOLA : That's quite true. Today, you're much nicer . . .

She puts a cigarette between her lips and hands the packet to RATH, *who fumbles and drops it on the floor.*

RATH : Oh . . . I'm sorry.

He bends down to pick up the cigarettes. Insert of the three schoolboys quietly closing the trap door. RATH *is on all fours under the table by* LOLA's *stockinged legs.* RATH *picks up the cigarettes scattered on the floor. In a medium shot,* LOLA *lights a cigarette, pulls at it and looks down.*

LOLA : Hey, Professor, when you've finished, send me a postcard, will you?

RATH, *under the table, keeps his eyes on* LOLA'S *legs.*
He misses two cigarettes as a result and turns round.
Close-up of RATH'S *head appearing above the table, on*
which he puts the cigarettes. He looks grotesque, his hair
dishevelled and his glasses crooked. In a medium shot,
RATH *kneels in front of* LOLA, *who smiles.*
LOLA : You are a sight! *She runs a comb through his hair*
and he recoils. No, keep still!
Holding his head with one hand, she combs his hair.
RATH *looks flustered. Steeply angled shot of the three*
boys looking through the trap door again.
LOLA *off* : Your boys should see you now!
A medium shot of the dressing room shows RATH *still*
kneeling in front of LOLA, *who hands him a box of*
powder.
LOLA *smiling* : And now to work.
Taking RATH *by the elbow, she helps him up and sits*
him down beside her. She powders her face while RATH
looks nervously around him.
LOLA : You really are . . . *She leans towards him; they appear*
face to face in medium close-up . . . rather sweet.
RATH *cannot bring himself to look at* LOLA. *He says*
nothing, but finally smiles at her; he is very flattered and
closes his eyes, shyly turning his head to one side. LOLA
immediately blows hard on the powder-box, covering
RATH'S *face and jacket with a thick cloud of powder.*
He jumps up and starts to cough as though about to
suffocate. LOLA *gaily brushes his coat and face, caressing*
his beard as she does so. RATH, *still coughing, takes off*
his glasses and wipes them. LOLA *tickles him under the*
chin. (Still on page 49)
LOLA *ironically and pityingly* : Does that hurt?
RATH *stops coughing. He blows, then realises that she*
is tickling him and smiles with childish satisfaction.
RATH *smiling* : No.
LOLA *pinching his cheek* : Is that better now?
RATH *laughing* : Oh yes!
Medium close-up from above on the half-open trap
door, as the three schoolboys look out. Suddenly, the

door opens and music is heard. The boys look towards the door. KIEPERT *is seen framed in the doorway.*
Another shot shows RATH *and* LOLA, RATH *looking very embarrassed at the sight of* KIEPERT. *He gets up.* LOLA *smiles.* RATH *moves back until he is next to the long mirror. He wipes his glasses and puts them on again, looking once more at* KIEPERT. *(Still on page 49) In increasing embarrassment, he dusts his coat, on which traces of powder can still be seen.* KIEPERT *approaches* LOLA. *She starts to do her hair while* KIEPERT *bows to* RATH.

KIEPERT : I am sorry to interrupt, Herr Professor. *He bends over* LOLA. What's going on here? Why aren't there any drinks being served? . . . There's a sailor out there with a wallet that's fit to burst. *(Still on page 50)*

LOLA : What's it got to do with me? Send out Guste!
In medium shot, RATH, *still dusting himself, listens to the conversation. Cut back to* LOLA *and* KIEPERT.

KIEPERT : Are you crazy? Who's going to buy champagne for Guste? It's you he wants.

LOLA : I won't. I'm an artiste, not a . . .

KIEPERT *speechless* : You're what?

LOLA : An artiste.

KIEPERT *looking at* RATH : Well, well . . . What do you make of that . . . *Cut to* RATH *as* KIEPERT *continues off* . . . Professor? The girl's got some crazy ideas about her profession!
A long shot towards the doorway shows the PROPRIETOR, *a large cigar in his mouth, carrying a bottle and an ice-bucket. He draws aside to admit a seaman, a* CAPTAIN *in uniform. The* CAPTAIN *almost fills the doorway. Obviously drunk, he makes his way towards the dressing table, while the* PROPRIETOR *shuts the door. Shot of the three of them together; the* CAPTAIN *moves towards* LOLA *while the* PROPRIETOR *puts down two glasses beside her.*

CAPTAIN : Good evening. . . . Here I am.
Cut to RATH, *who looks at* KIEPERT *in astonishment as the* CAPTAIN *speaks.*

CAPTAIN *off* : I've just arrived from Calcutta.
Cut to LOLA *and the* CAPTAIN, *facing one another. The*

CAPTAIN *produces a pineapple and deposits it on the table.*

CAPTAIN : Part of my cargo. . .

He takes LOLA'S *hand and tries to kiss it, but she snatches it away hastily.*

LOLA : Leave me alone.

The PROPRIETOR *uncorks the bottle and fills the glasses.*

LOLA : Get out!

The PROPRIETOR *glares at her and nudges her furiously with his elbow. The* CAPTAIN *leans towards* LOLA.

CAPTAIN : But I haven't done anything to you!

Medium shot of RATH *and* KIEPERT. *The latter restrains* RATH *from hurling himself at the* CAPTAIN. RATH *breaks free and pushes the* CAPTAIN.

RATH : Wretch! . . . Get out!

CAPTAIN *very surprised, to* LOLA : Who's this, your papa?

RATH *scandalised* : How dare you molest this lady!

CAPTAIN *ironically* : Are you the lady's father?

Members of the troupe appear in the doorway.

KIEPERT *off* : But . . . Herr Professor!

RATH *off* : Silence . . . Silence, I say! *Resume on* RATH *and* KIEPERT . . . Miserable procurer!

CAPTAIN : Who me? A procurer?

RATH : Yes. Get out! . . . Out! . . . Out!

The camera pans as RATH *pushes the* CAPTAIN *out of the dressing room and shuts the door. Medium close-up of the* CLOWN *standing at the other door with the chorus-girls. All have been watching the scene in silence. Cut back to* RATH *and to* LOLA *at her dressing table.* KIEPERT *throws himself on* RATH.

KIEPERT *beside himself with indignation* : But what right have you to . . . ?

RATH *slaps him violently a couple of times. Cut to the* CLOWN *and the girls looking on in astonishment. They disappear behind the door. Return to* RATH *and* KIEPERT, *face to face.*

RATH : Miserable procurer!

The PROPRIETOR *enters the picture, pushes* KIEPERT *out of the way and plants himself in front of* RATH.

PROPRIETOR: Just what the hell's the idea of chucking everyone out, eh? *He brandishes the champagne bottle.* The fellow had paid for the bottle!
As he waves the bottle, he manages to pour some of its contents over KIEPERT.
RATH *haughtily*: I'll pay for everything!
In medium shot, LOLA *looks on in astonishment. She leans back and stretches out one leg, revealing her stocking on her thigh.*
RATH *off*: Get out!
Noises outside the dressing room: the voice of the CAPTAIN *can be heard.*
CAPTAIN *off*: He called me a procurer!
In medium shot outside LOLA'S *dressing room, the* CAPTAIN *is standing on the steps which lead up to the stage, waving his arms and shouting. The* PROPRIETOR *rushes towards him and tries to restrain him.*
CAPTAIN *bellowing*: Procurer!
PROPRIETOR: You're crazy, Captain . . . Don't make a racket here! *He bangs the palm of his hand on the stair-rail.* You'll have the police on my neck.
CAPTAIN *as loudly as ever*: Yes, the police . . . I'll go and get the police . . . You old crook!
He struggles with the PROPRIETOR, *breaks free and goes up the steps.* GUSTE *is seen standing at the entrance to the stage, holding a glass of beer. The* CAPTAIN *knocks into her, upsetting the beer.*
The stage is seen from the front: the CAPTAIN *leaps into view.*
CAPTAIN: The crook! Call the police!
The PROPRIETOR *follows him on. Long shot of the stage as the* CAPTAIN *staggers forward, waving his arms, and divides the front and hind part of a stage horse.*
CAPTAIN *bellowing*: He tried to knock me over!
KIEPERT, *in front of the door into* LOLA'S *dressing room, buries his head in his hands in despair. In* LOLA'S *dressing room,* RATH *is sitting down, holding the bottle.* LOLA *stands beside him, wearing a black costume with a transparent skirt revealing black-frilled knickers.*

63

LOLA *impressed*: Someone fighting over me? *Surprised and genuinely pleased*. That hasn't happened for a long time!
She takes the bottle from RATH.
RATH *very sure of himself*: I only did my duty.
LOLA *puts the bottle on the table and goes up to* RATH. *The camera pans as she turns around him, caressing his shoulders with her hands. He fidgets.*
LOLA: Now, now, there's no need to get worked up again, Professor. *She picks up the two glasses and hands one of them to* RATH. Now we must wash it down. *She raises her glass and smiles*. Cheers!
RATH: May I . . . ? *He drinks*. Your health . . . Your very good health!
They drink. Still standing, LOLA *looks at* RATH *and smiles.*
The camera pans, then tracks forwards from the entrance of THE BLUE ANGEL *into the club itself, following the arrival of a policeman. He moves towards the stage, increasingly concealed by fishing nets and decorations. The audience, sitting around him, drink and smoke and talk loudly. In the background is a poster of 'LOLA-LOLA' on the wall. In medium shot, the* PROPRIETOR, *aided by a waiter and some stage hands, tries to remove the* CAPTAIN *from the stage. In a long shot across the club, the audience is seen in the background, with the* POLICEMAN, *his hands behind his back, advancing slowly towards the stage. Cut to* KIEPERT *in the wings. He looks out at the stage and the audience, hesitates, then rushes towards the door to the dressing room and goes through. Inside* LOLA's *dressing room,* KIEPERT *comes face to face with* RATH *and* LOLA, *and raises his hat.*
KIEPERT *very excited*: I'm sorry . . . Herr . . . Herr Professor, but . . . the police are here.
RATH *uneasily*: The police! . . . The police. . . .
KIEPERT *hands* RATH *his hat.*
KIEPERT: They musn't find you here!
RATH *pulling himself together*: I have nothing to fear from the authorities.
KIEPERT: You haven't, but we have.

64

KIEPERT *moves rapidly out of frame.* LOLA, *who has been listening at the door, takes* RATH *by the arm.*

LOLA : You'd better disappear, Professor.

Pan as she pushes him towards the trap door into the cellar, which KIEPERT *has just opened.* LOLA *pushes* RATH *down through the trap door. Half-way through, he turns round to protest once more.*

RATH : I have nothing to fear from the authorities.

He disappears.

LOLA *and* KIEPERT *shut the trap door and breathe a sigh of relief.* KIEPERT *mops his brow.*

LOLA *amused* : We'll end up opening a boarding-house down there!

In the wings, in front of LOLA'S *door,* GUSTE *tries to keep back the* POLICEMAN. *Standing nearby are the* PROPRIETOR, *the* CAPTAIN, *now a little more sober, the* CLOWN, *stage-hands and various onlookers, all talking at once. There is general pandemonium.*

POLICEMAN *severely* : Keep calm for a moment, can't you?

The POLICEMAN *opens the door into* LOLA'S *dressing room, and goes in. From inside the room, medium shot of the* PROPRIETOR *and the* CAPTAIN *standing in the doorway, the latter containing his rage with difficulty. They both move forward and a stage-hand shuts the door behind them. In a group shot,* LOLA, KIEPERT *and the* POLICEMAN.

POLICEMAN *indicating the* CAPTAIN : This gentleman claims he was assaulted in this very room.

Group shot of all four.

CAPTAIN : He tried to knock me down. . . . Knock me down, I tell you!

LOLA *puts on a gleaming white top hat, apparently indifferent to the whole proceedings.*

KIEPERT : Who?

POLICEMAN *very calm* : Yes, who?

GUSTE *enters the picture, carrying a glass of beer. The* CAPTAIN *looks around, searching for* RATH.

CAPTAIN : What's happened to the . . . er . . . gangster?

GUSTE *pointing at the* CAPTAIN : That's the one, Officer. He

69

attacked me on the stage.

POLICEMAN *moving away from her* : All right, that's enough.
I don't want any more wild accusations.

He pushes past GUSTE *and* KIEPERT *and goes to the
other end of the room. Pan as he crosses the room and
passes in front of the mirror.*

CAPTAIN *off* : Where have you hidden him, you crook?

PROPRIETOR : How should I know, you crazy drunkard, I
wasn't even there!

The POLICEMAN *goes to the staircase, glances upwards
and climbs a few steps towards* LOLA'S *bedroom.*

RATH *off, in a muffled voice* : Here! Come here!

The POLICEMAN *stops and turns round. Medium shot of
the* CAPTAIN, *who also looks round, and realises that the
voice is coming from under the floor.*

RATH : Little wretches! . . . I've caught you at last!

In the centre of the room, the trap door opens and
LOHMANN *emerges, followed by a furious* RATH *pulling*
GOLDSTAUB *through the opening.*

RATH : Come on, come on, out you come! At last I've caught
you. It's all over. Come on, up! *He turns back and catches
hold of* ERTZUM. You too, up! Rascals! *He pushes them
against the wall and bellows.* Guttersnipes!

The POLICEMAN *goes over and looks down into the cellar,
then lowers the trap door, while the* CAPTAIN *points an
accusing finger at* RATH. *The latter, covered in dust, puts
on a dignified air and pulls down his cuffs.*

CAPTAIN : That's him. He's the one who tried to knock me
down! It's him, officer, it's him!

The POLICEMAN *goes up to* RATH *and salutes.*

POLICEMAN : Excuse me, Herr Professor.

CAPTAIN *coming forward and pointing at* RATH : He called
me a procurer!

POLICEMAN *pushing him away* : Silence. *To* RATH. Excuse me,
Herr Professor . . . This man wants to prefer a charge.

*Group shot of the three men and the schoolboys. (Still
on page 51)*

RATH *gesticulating* : Prefer a charge! *He turns to his pupils standing behind him.* I've got a charge or two to prefer as well!

CAPTAIN *to the* POLICEMAN : What's all this about preferring charges? Arrest the man.

POLICEMAN *pushing him back* : Will you shut up once and for all!

CAPTAIN : Nobody's going to make me shut up!

POLICEMAN *taking him by the arm* : We'll see about that. Come on, off to the police station.

CAPTAIN *towards* RATH : He tried to knock me down!
A new angle shows LOLA *and the* CLOWN *standing to the left, watching the scene. On the right,* GUSTE *looks on sadly, still holding her glass of beer. Behind stands* KIEPERT.

CAPTAIN *off* : He called me a procurer!
Waiters and stage-hands stand in the wings outside LOLA'S *door. Loud music. The* POLICEMAN *passes through, pushing the* CAPTAIN *in front of him.*

Back in LOLA'S *dressing room* RATH *strides to and fro in front of the three schoolboys, who are lined up against the wall. They — and particularly* LOHMANN — *do not look especially worried, but stand watching* RATH *rather contemptuously.* LOHMANN *produces a cigarette.*

RATH *indignant* : You realise what the consequences of this incident will be for you? *He stops, furious, in front of* LOH-MANN, *who is nonchalantly lighting his cigarette.* Take that cigarette out of your mouth! LOHMANN, *looking amused, blows smoke in* RATH'S *face;* RATH *seethes with anger.* Take that cigarette out of your mouth!

LOHMANN *stares insolently at* RATH, *who strikes the cigarette from his mouth and turns to the other two, who are standing and sniggering.*

RATH : Confess! . . . What do you come here for?
Cut to LOLA, *who turns first to* KIEPERT, *then to* GUSTE.

GOLDSTAUB *in medium close-up* : The same thing as you, Herr Professor!

A new shot of RATH *with the three schoolboys shows the schoolmaster slapping* GOLDSTAUB *violently, then* ERTZUM, *before pushing them towards the door.*

71

RATH *shouting*: Out! . . . Out! . . . Out!

The schoolboys flee towards the exit.

In long shot outside LOLA'S *dressing room, the school-boys run down the corridor, silhouetted against the wall. Music.*

RATH *off*: You haven't heard the last of this!

Back in LOLA'S *dressing room, the* CLOWN *leans against the mirror. He turns round with a bitter expression and goes out, shutting the door behind him. Medium shot of* RATH *coming back towards the middle of the room, straightening his glasses. Pan to* GUSTE, *who goes towards him and pats him on the shoulder.*

GUSTE: You did the right thing, ducky! Now push this drink behind your necktie.

She hands him her glass of beer; he takes a large gulp from it. There is a loud noise outside, as the window is flung open. Cut to the window and the faces of the three schoolboys yelling in its frame.

SCHOOLBOYS: Unrath! . . . Unrath! (Excrement!)

They disappear. Cut back to RATH, *who puts down his glass and snatches it up again, upsetting some beer in the process; he then bumps into* GUSTE *and rushes to the window.*

RATH *leans from the window and waves his hand with the glass, threateningly after the boys, who have disappeared. As he bellows after them, his gestures become more and more jerky and mechanical. The beer spills on the ground.*

RATH *uncontrollably*: Little devils! You haven't heard the last of this! . . . You have . . . *His voice breaks, he tries again.* You ha . . . *Much less loudly* . . . You haven't heard the last of this! *His voice fades away.* You haven't heard . . . You haven't . . .

He puts his hand to his heart, groans and staggers.

Cut back to the dressing room from the inside; LOLA *runs across to* RATH *and holds him up, helped by* GUSTE. *Pan as they carry him to a chair. Medium shot of* RATH, *slightly from above. He sits in a chair, his eyes closed, gasping for breath. The two women lean over him.*

(Still on page 51) LOLA *takes his hat off.*
LOLA *anxiously*: But . . . for heaven's sake, what's the matter?
He tries to reply. GUSTE *looks towards the* CLOWN.
RATH: It will soon pass . . . It will . . . *He puts his hand to his heart.* I feel better already.
GUSTE: The little hooligans! *A pause.* You've certainly chosen a fine profession.
LOLA *patting him on the back*: You just got overexcited . . . You shouldn't do that . . .
    She strokes RATH'S *hair. The bell rings to call her on-stage.* RATH *leans towards her, but she moves away.*
LOLA: Damn that bell!
    Cut to the PROPRIETOR, *who strides in angrily through the stage door. Music is heard off, and there is a loud discontented hubbub from the audience. The* PROPRIETOR *addresses* KIEPERT.
PROPRIETOR: What's going on here? The place is half empty!
KIEPERT: Oh, quit complaining! Who brought the Captain in, anyway? *To* LOLA. Come on! *He gestures towards the door.* Get moving.
    LOLA *nods, goes up to* RATH *and looks him in the eye.*
LOLA: Come outside, Professor. . . . Come and listen. *She leans towards him and tickles him under the chin, smiling.* I'll soon put you right. *(Still on page 52) Pan as she moves towards the door.* Yes! . . .
    The PROPRIETOR *is seen standing outside* LOLA'S *door.* LOLA'S *leg appears stretched out horizontally through the doorway. He looks at it with interest.* LOLA *herself appears and shuts the door, smiling. There are whistles from the audience, off, and the band begins to play the tune of* 'Falling in Love Again' (Ich bin von Kopf bis Fuss). LOLA *taps her top hat and goes onstage, smiling. Sitting at* LOLA'S *table,* RATH *looks at* KIEPERT, *who goes over to an upended suitcase on which there are several bottles. He fills a glass and addresses* RATH.
KIEPERT *filling the glass*: You gave me a bit of a punch, but I'm not the kind to bear a grudge . . . *He comes towards* RATH *holding the glass; the* CLOWN *can be seen in the background, watching them.* I'm going to give you a bit of my own

73

personal medicine . . . *He picks up one of the champagne glasses and empties into it the glass, which he already has in his hand.* There we are. Drink it, it'll put soup in your bones. RATH *looking curiously at the glass and then at* KIEPERT : You really think it will do me good?

KIEPERT : Right! It'll bolster you up a bit.

RATH *empties the glass in one gulp and starts to cough violently. The* CLOWN *and* KIEPERT *watch him as he takes a deep breath and smiles.*

KIEPERT : Okay?

RATH *nodding, slightly hoarse* : Yes!

KIEPERT : Right, now you can show your face again. *He takes* RATH *by the arm.* Come on!

RATH : Where to?

KIEPERT : To the celebrities' box.

RATH : What for?

KIEPERT : Don't you want to hear Lola sing?

RATH : Lola?

KIEPERT : Yes.

RATH *happily* : Ah yes, Lola!

KIEPERT *takes him by the arm and leads him out.*

Inside the club, the camera pans from the audience towards the stage, where LOLA *is singing in her white top hat. Behind her sit* GUSTE *and the other woman. Fishing nets and an anchor are hanging over the stage.*

LOLA *singing* : Ein rätselhafter Schimmer, *(Still on page 52)*

    Ein je-ne-sais-pas-quoi,

    Liegt in den Augen immer

    Bei einer schönen Frau!

    (An enigmatic glimmer

    A je-ne-sais-pas-quoi

    Shines always in the glance

    Of a pretty woman.)

From a distance, the camera pans to follow RATH, KIEPERT *and the* CLOWN *coming into the club from the side.* KIEPERT *pushes* RATH, *who is listening and watching in fascination, past a statue in front of the band and past some standing people, towards a reserved table in a box at the top of some steps. On the way up,* RATH

74

stops, his eyes glued to the stage. Pan upwards as KIE-
PERT *pushes him on.*
LOLA *singing off* : Doch wenn sich meine Augen
Bei einem vis-a-vis
Ganz tief in seine saugen,
Was sagen dann die?
(But when my eyes look deeply
At my vis-a-vis
And gaze intently at him
What does it mean?)
KIEPERT *off* : Stop! . . . Your attention, please!
LOLA *looks up towards* RATH. *In a reverse shot,* RATH
*is seen sitting in the box on a balcony, with his hands on
the balustrade.* KIEPERT *stands behind him, holding his
top hat. (Still on page 53)*
KIEPERT *coming forward* : Ladies . . .
Medium close-up on a bewildered RATH. *He squints
down at the audience.*
KIEPERT *partly off* : . . . and gentlemen, may I have the
pleasure . . .
Cut to a long shot of the stage, then pan as LOLA *moves
across the footlights, shielding her eyes from the glare.
She looks up at the balcony. The camera, following her
gaze, pans back to* RATH *and* KIEPERT.
KIEPERT *continuing* : . . . of presenting to you this evening's
guest of honour, Doctor Immanuel . . .
Medium close-up of RATH *looking a little self-conscious,
but nevertheless proud. He gives a little wave to the
audience.*
KIEPERT *continuing* : . . . Rath, Professor. *Pan towards the
audience, all looking up expectantly at the balcony* . . . at the
local university.
VOICES IN THE AUDIENCE : Oh! . . . Well! . . . Oh! . . . Well
now! . . . Hurrah!
*The camera tilts down onto the audience, who are laugh-
ing and clapping noisily. Close-up of* RATH, *smiling and
much flattered by his ovation. A pause, then a shot of*
LOLA *on the stage, also clapping. Long shot of the stage,
slightly from below, as* GUSTE *raises her glass in a toast*

to RATH, *while* LOLA *applauds. Then pan with* LOLA *as she thrusts her hips forward and goes nonchalantly back to the centre of the stage, winking at one of the girls at the back, who immediately gets up.* LOLA *takes her chair and sits astride it, leaning on the back. Crossing her legs and throwing a suggestive glance up at the balcony, she begins to sing, underlining each phrase with a provocative gesture.*

LOLA *singing* : Falling in love again
Never wanted to . . .

In a medium shot of the celebrities' box, the enthralled RATH *listens as* LOLA *continues to sing.* KIEPERT *stands beside him, his hands in his pockets, noting* RATH'S *reaction. (Still on page 54) After a few moments, he taps his head and moves away, unnoticed by* RATH.

LOLA *off* : What am I to do
Can't help it
Love's always been my game
Play it how I may
I was made that way
Can't help it

She throws her head back, eyes half-closed.
Men cluster to me . . .

In a long shot, the CLOWN *stands by the band, looking on.*

LOLA *off* : Like moths around a flame . . .

Pan upwards, taking in a life-size wooden statue of a naked woman in the form of a figurehead. The camera comes to rest on RATH, *who is smiling.*

LOLA *off* : And if their wings burn
I know I'm not to blame.

RATH *looks with interest at the statue, which almost reaches the top of the box.*

LOLA *off* : Falling in love again,
Never wanted to —
What am I to do?
Can't . . .

RATH *turns his attention back to the stage . . .*
help . . .

76

Cut to LOLA, *smiling . . .*
it.
As RATH *smiles happily in medium shot, the audience applauds off. Looking embarrassed, he puts a hand to his face, to hide his pleasure from the audience and smiles at* LOLA, *who starts to sing an encore, as the room hushes.*

LOLA *off* : Falling in . . .
She taps her top hat in medium shot.
. . . love again,
Never wanted to . . .
She opens her arms wide. (Still on page 55)
What am I to do?
Can't help it.
Cut back to a delighted RATH, *then back to* LOLA.
Love's always been my game
Play it how I may
I was made that way
Can't help it
Men cluster to me
Like moths around a flame,
And if their wings burn,
I know I'm not to blame.
She shakes her head and smiles. (Still on page 55)
Falling in love again,
Never wanted to . . .
Cut to RATH, *attentive and smiling. He runs his fingers round under his collar, then puts a hand up to hide his self-satisfied smile from the audience. His smile becomes almost a grimace.*

LOLA *off* : What am I to do?
Can't help it.
(Ich bin von Kopf bis Fuss auf Liebe eingestellt
Denn das ist meine Welt und sonst gar nichts
Das ist — was soll ich machen — meine Natur
Ich kann halt lieben nur und sonst gar nichts
Männer umschwirren mich wie Motten um
   das Licht
Und wenn sie verbrennen dafür kann ich nichts

Ich bin von Kopf bis Fuss auf Liebe eingestellt
Denn das ist meine Welt und sonst gar nichts)
In RATH's *bedroom, close-up on a motto hanging above the bed with the inscription,* 'Be just and fear no one.' *There is a knock at the door.*

MAID *off* : Herr Professor?

The camera tracks backwards to reveal the bed, which has not been slept in. A ray of sunlight falls across it from the window. On a shelf above the bed is a row of books; there are more books piled on the bedside table.

MAID *insistently, off* : Breakfast! . . .

Cut to a shot of the MAID *as she opens the door and goes to the bed. Finding it empty, she looks around her in bewilderment.*

In LOLA's *bedroom,* RATH *is stretched out on the bed, snoring, with a doll in his arms. His waistcoat is hanging loosely from his right arm, his shirt collar is undone and he is still wearing his trousers. After some moments, he wakes, sits up on the bed and looks around the room, as if wondering where he is. He sits on the edge of the bed, looks at the doll which he still has in his hand, and pushes its arm down, letting off a musical chime. He puts the doll to his ear; the chime stops. Intrigued, he picks up his glasses. The chime starts again and then stops.* RATH *throws the doll down on the bed behind him. The chime starts again for a few seconds, then a bird is heard singing.* RATH *looks up and smiles. Cut to a shot of a bird cage, in which a small bird is twittering and hopping about. A new shot shows* LOLA *in a dressing gown, standing by the table in the centre of the room; breakfast is laid. She is holding a coffee pot and turns towards* RATH *and smiles.*

LOLA : 'Morning, Immanuel.

RATH *in medium close-up* : Good morning.

He gives a little bow and straightens his bow tie. Cut back to LOLA, *who strikes a cup with a teaspoon, making it ring.*

LOLA : Breakfast is served, Herr Professor!

RATH *has got up. He puts on his waistcoat, buttons it up, runs his fingers through his hair and picks up his coat from the back of a chair. The bird is heard chirruping off. Pan towards* LOLA, *who goes towards* RATH *and takes him by the hand.*

LOLA : Come on, sweetie, the coffee'll be cold.

She leads him across to the table, helping him on with his coat. He combs his hair.

LOLA : There, sit down.

As he sits down, she goes round behind him, takes the comb from him, sits down, puts the comb on the table and picks up the milk jug. Medium shot of the two of them sitting together at the table. LOLA *pours* RATH *some milk. He looks at her and smiles. She smiles back.*

LOLA : Tell me, sweetheart, do you always snore so much?

RATH *rubbing his eyes* : I'm afraid I rather overdid it last night.

LOLA *pouring herself some milk* : Ah yes! Two bottles of champagne. You held it very well.

RATH *smiles, flattered.* LOLA *takes some sugar.* RATH *gazes at her, fascinated.*

LOLA *taking a lump of sugar and holding it over* RATH'S *cup* : One?

RATH *gazes at her without replying, so she drops the lump into the cup and takes another one.*

LOLA : Two?

RATH : Three!

She drops another lump into the cup.

LOLA *winking at him* : You really are a sweet one.

The bird chirrups. RATH *stirs his coffee and drinks.*

LOLA : Is it all right?

RATH : Excellent! Remarkably good!

LOLA *waving a knife* : You see . . . you could do this every day.

RATH *looks at her lovingly. The bird chirrups again.*

RATH : There's no reason why not. *He ponders. . . .* Since I'm a bachelor.

LOLA *leans back in her chair astonished.* RATH *drinks his coffee. At that moment the carillon of the town clock, playing 'Ueb immer Treu und Redlichkeit' can be heard in the distance.* RATH *looks over the edge of his cup at the camera. He puts the cup down. The clock strikes eight. He takes out his watch and looks at it.*

RATH *excitedly*: I must be off to school. *He gets up.* I must hurry.

In the class-room, LOHMANN, *seen in long shot with his back to the camera, is drawing a caricature of* RATH *on the board. He represents him as an angel with a halo, floating among clouds and playing a lyre, from which emerge the words 'LOLA-LOLA'. As he draws,* LOHMANN *glances continually towards the door. A shot of one corner of the classroom shows* ANGST, *gagged and struggling, being firmly held down by* ERTZUM. *Cut back to* LOHMANN, *who finishes his drawing, adding long hairs to* RATH's *legs.*

Back in LOLA's *bedroom,* RATH *stands with his hat and coat on, cane in hand; he looks excited.* LOLA *comes up to him with a carnation in her hand.*

LOLA : Come here! *She draws him to her.* Keep still. *She puts the carnation in his buttonhole.* There, that's so you'll think of me.

She tries to kiss him on the cheek, but he hurries away. The camera pans after him as he goes past her out of the room and down the stairs.

LOLA : Aren't you going to say good-bye to me?

RATH *does not raise his head.* LOLA *kneels down and leans over the stair-rail.*

LOLA : Kiss me once more!

RATH *puts his head between the bars of the staircase. She kisses him.*

LOLA : Do you still love me?

RATH *plaintively*: Yes . . . yes, of course . . . yes. Good-bye. *He goes on down.*

LOLA *watching him go* : And be careful of the trams!

Long shot across LOLA's *dressing room: two maids watch* RATH *coming down the stairs.*

ONE OF THE MAIDS : 'Morning, Herr Professor.

RATH : Good morning.

80

He looks round, annoyed, and goes out. Fade out.
A long shot of the school clock shows the time as ten past eight. Above the clock face is the motto ' ORA ET LABORA.' Pan downwards as RATH *hurries into the main entrance of the school.*
RATH, *having taken off his coat, goes towards the door of his classroom in long shot. He hesitates for a moment before entering, bends down, puts his ear to the door, straightens up, looks around him, then finally goes into the room.*
A long medium shot across the room from the inside catches RATH *as he comes in through the door. All the pupils get up. Pan as* RATH *goes to his desk.*
RATH : Sit down!
The pupils sit down. The camera pans across one side of the blackboard which has another drawing on it showing RATH *in frock coat and top hat, carrying one of* LOLA'S *legs over his shoulder. Very slow pan across the blackboard to* LOHMANN'S *drawing of* RATH *as an angel. The words ' LOLA-LOLA ' have been repeated several times.* RATH, *having seen the drawings, now looks furiously at the class, obviously controlling himself with difficulty. He takes the board rubber and begins to rub out the first drawing with hasty, sweeping strokes. At that moment,* ERTZUM, *his back to the camera, gets up from his desk at the front of the middle row.*
ERTZUM *shouting* : Please Sir . . . this place stinks of Unrath! (Excrement!)
He turns to the rest of the class, seeking their agreement.
ERTZUM *very loudly* : Unrath! . . . Unrath!
Seen in a long shot with his pupils, RATH *stands with the board rubber in his hand. (Still on page 56) The situation seems beyond his control and he gapes at the class which is now yelling in a frenzy. There are whistles and laughter, and the word ' UNRATH ' is shouted again and again. A long shot down the corridor outside the classroom, shows several other masters, alarmed by the shouting, as they gather outside the door and listen to the uproar inside. After a few moments, the* HEAD-

MASTER *appears at the top of a staircase. He hurries up to the door.*

Inside the classroom, the camera pans across, as the HEADMASTER *comes in through the door. The pupils are still yelling and whistling, while* RATH *is standing beside his desk as before, trembling with rage and shouting at the boys.*

RATH *shouting*: Be quiet! . . . Be quiet! I'll have you all locked up, you devils!

On seeing the HEADMASTER, *the pupils fall silent and go back to their places.* RATH *also stops shouting and looks at the* HEADMASTER.

HEADMASTER *to the class*: Outside, all of you. You'll be dealt with later.

Very quietly, the pupils leave the room.

Outside in the corridor, they are seen emerging, while the other masters turn and go back to their classes.

Inside RATH'S *classroom, pan towards* RATH *and the* HEADMASTER, *who have been watching the pupils file out of the room. The* HEADMASTER *then turns towards* RATH *and watches him as he puts the board rubber down on the desk, takes out a handkerchief and cleans his hands. The* HEADMASTER *walks round the desk to the blackboard and looks at the drawings.*

HEADMASTER: Not without talent!

As he speaks, the HEADMASTER *goes up to* RATH, *looks him up and down, and removes the carnation from his buttonhole. Medium shot of the pair of them face to face.* RATH *puts on his glasses, while the* HEADMASTER *sniffs at the carnation and then hands it back to him.*

HEADMASTER *taking off his pince-nez*: I understand the situation completely . . . but how can you risk your whole career for the sake of a creature like that?

RATH *angrily*: Headmaster, I must forbid this . . . You are speaking of my future wife!

HEADMASTER *incredulously*: You can't be serious!

RATH *puffing out his chest*: I couldn't be more serious. I won't hear another word.

The HEADMASTER *gives* RATH *a long and searching look,*

*then turns away with a gesture of resignation. A new
shot shows him near the door.*

HEADMASTER: I am extremely sorry, my dear colleague . . .
but in that case, I am afraid we can hardly let the matter
rest there.

*He goes out, his face serious and decided. Pan towards
RATH standing at the blackboard, in front of the caricature of himself as an ' angel'. Slowly he goes to his
chair, puts the carnation down on the desk and sits down
heavily. After a while, he opens a drawer and puts into
it the class exercise book. A new shot of RATH, full face:
he takes from the drawer his little black notebook and
an open penknife, which he puts on the desk. He looks
at the notebook for a few moments, then puts it in the
inside pocket of his coat. He pauses, then picks up the
penknife, closes it and puts it in his trouser pocket.
Finally, he gathers up his books. In a medium long shot
across the empty classroom, RATH is seen standing behind
his desk. He puts down the books and, looking at the
carnation, sinks back onto the chair. He seems very tired.
The camera tracks backwards, taking in the empty seats.
Fade out.*

LOLA'S *dressing room is in complete disorder. There are
suitcases everywhere.* KIEPERT, *a cigar between his teeth,
walks up and down the room. A woman passes, her arms
full.* GUSTE *is scurrying about. All three are in travelling
clothes.*

KIEPERT: Get a move on and pack your things, will you?
. . . You'll make us miss the train.

GUSTE *shrugs and takes a cigarette. There is a knock at
the door.*

KIEPERT: Come in.

The door opens on RATH, *looking very formal. He is
wearing a top hat and carrying a large bouquet of
white roses.*

KIEPERT: 'Morning, Professor. *Bumping into* GUSTE. Haven't
you got anything better to do than stand around here? . . .
I really wonder why I ever married you.

GUSTE *tossing her head*: I've racked my brains asking myself that, too!

KIEPERT *to* RATH: What are you standing around for? *Indicating the staircase.* Go on up. You know the way, don't you?

Very slowly, RATH climbs the stairs.

In her bedroom, LOLA is seen from behind, bending over the bed and packing a suitcase. She is wearing travelling clothes. Medium shot of RATH'S head as he appears at the top of the staircase. He comes up into the room and looks around. Cut back to LOLA, who hears him and turns round.

LOLA: How nice of you to come and say good-bye to me.

She carries on packing. Cut back to RATH, standing stiffly, holding his flowers. (Still on page 56)

RATH *hesitantly*: Dear Miss Lola, I . . .

Return to LOLA who straightens up and comes towards RATH. A new shot shows the pair of them face to face.

LOLA: Oh! What lovely flowers! *She takes them and kisses him on the cheek.* Thank you.

LOLA moves out of the picture. Another shot shows her by the bed; she turns and smiles. Medium shot of RATH, twisting his hat in his hands; he looks extremely embarrassed. Return to LOLA, who sniffs the bouquet; feels that she has thanked him too little, and puts the flowers on the bed and comes towards him. Shot of the pair of them face to face.

LOLA: There's no need to look so sad! I'll return next year.

RATH: Dear Miss Lola, I have brought you something else.

He feels in his pocket and brings out a small box, which he holds out to her.

RATH: Would you . . . *Medium shot of LOLA, looking very surprised, as he continues off . . .* accept this present from me?

LOLA takes the box and opens it. There is a ring inside. She is amazed. She takes the ring out of the box and slips it onto her finger.

RATH *off*: And may I at the same time ask . . . *Medium shot of both of them . . .* for your hand?

LOLA *looking frankly sceptical*: You want to marry me?

RATH *sincerely*: Yes.

84

LOLA *immediately doubles up with laughter. The camera pans as she puts her hand over her mouth and moves a short distance away from* RATH. *Still laughing, she opens her arms and comes back towards him, then takes his hat and cane and puts them on the table. She calms down slightly and tries to take him in her arms. He draws back and gazes at her intently.*

LOLA : God, you are sweet!

RATH : I hope, my child, that you are fully conscious of the gravity of this moment.

LOLA *calms down completely and for the first time seems extremely embarrassed. She looks at* RATH *for a moment in silence. He puts his arm round her shoulders and draws her to him.* LOLA *smiles and presses herself against him. They kiss.*

With a group, LOLA, *dressed in bridal costume is leaning on* RATH'S *shoulder, and smiling at him as they listen to a piano playing Mendelssohn's 'Wedding March.' They are seated at a table covered with bottles and glasses. Voices are heard off — particularly* KIE-PERT'S *— singing and cheering. The next shot shows the company assembled round the table, which is loaded with the remains of the wedding feast. All the members of the troupe are present with* KIEPERT *acting as cheer-leader.* LOLA *and* RATH *are on his left and* RATH *has his arm round his wife, who looks very happy and takes his hand tenderly. Several times the guests rise to their feet with glasses in their hands and toast.* LOLA *and* RATH *rise, too. They all sit down again, except for* KIEPERT, *who remains standing. The piano stops.*

KIEPERT : Ladies . . . and gentlemen. To-day, it gives me very great pleasure . . .

GUSTE *getting up* : Stop! *Weeping with emotion.* Can't you stop blathering for one moment?

KIEPERT *sitting down with a shrug* : Here we go again!

Medium shot of GUSTE, *who is now standing behind* RATH *and* LOLA.

GUSTE : It was wonderful when I got married, too. *To* RATH. If I'd known you then, perhaps I'd have been a schoolmaster's wife, too. Now all I've got for a husband is a conjuror.

KIEPERT *leaping to his feet* : Yes, I am indeed a conjuror!

GUSTE : Now we're in for some more of his pathetic tricks.

KIEPERT : Sit down, will you? *She sits.* You're not going to prevent me giving the Professor a demonstration of my art. *To* RATH. I will now take the liberty . . . of producing a few eggs from under your nose. Look, my hands are empty.

> *He takes hold of* RATH'S *nose, and suddenly an egg appears in his hand. There is a fanfare, followed by applause.*

KIEPERT *giving* RATH *the egg* : There, take it! Now, I'll produce a second egg. Now, Professor, watch carefully.

> *He produces another egg from under* RATH'S *nose. (Still on page 65) Again there is a fanfare and applause.* KIEPERT *gives* RATH *the second egg and sits down.* LOLA *looks sideways at* RATH *and begins to cluck like a hen.* RATH *sits holding the two eggs. At first he looks surprised, then grinning happily, he suddenly crows like a cock.*

RATH *upright in his seat* : Kick-a-rick-ki!

> *A new shot of* RATH, *smiling happily at* LOLA, *who clucks away.*

RATH : Kick-a-rick-ki!

> *Applause and laughter, as* RATH *looks pleased with himself and crows again for effect.*
>
> LOLA, *watching* KIEPERT, *bursts out laughing.* RATH *hugs and kisses her. Fade out.*
>
> *In a hotel room,* RATH *walks up and down near a curtain behind which* LOLA *is changing her clothes. She can be seen in silhouette.* RATH *goes and looks through the curtain. He smiles, looking very pleased with himself and puffing out his chest. Then, scratching the back of his neck, he sits down on a divan, takes a puff at his cigarette and inhales deeply. In medium close-up,* LOLA *pokes her head out from behind the curtain.*

LOLA : Give me the small case, will you, sweetheart?

> RATH *scrambles to his feet. A second shot shows him standing in front of a pile of suitcases. Taking the top one, he turns out the contents on the floor. The camera tilts down onto postcards of* LOLA *scattered on the carpet.*

90

Cut to LOLA, *half-hidden behind the curtain. She watches* RATH, *smiling.*

LOLA: You are hopeless!

High-angle shot of RATH *kneeling on the floor. He puts his cigarette in his mouth and picks up the cards.*

RATH: Why did you bring these postcards?

Cut to LOLA.

LOLA: What a stupid question! They're sold every evening.

RATH *shot from above*: So long as I have a single penny . . .

Cut to LOLA, *as* RATH *continues off* . . . they will not be sold!

LOLA: All right . . . but you'd better pick them up . . . one never knows.

She disappears behind the curtain. Fade out.

A night-club interior: RATH *is sitting at a small table by a poster of ' LOLA-LOLA '. Sounds of applause. He turns his head towards the camera and puffs at the fag-end of a cigarette. His hair and beard are dishevelled, and he looks generally in a pitiful state. (Still on page 65)*

LOLA *singing off*:

Nimm dich in Acht vor blonden Frauen
Die haben so etwas gewisses
S'ist ihnen nicht gleich anzuschauen
Aber irgend etwas ist es
(Take care of women who have blonde hair
They have a special flair
They have no way of being fair
They'll strip you and leave you bare)

RATH *turns round. He looks weary.*

LOLA *singing off*:

Ein kleines Blickgeplänkel sei erlaubt dir
(Stare all you please but do no more than look)

RATH *pulls a packet of photographs of* LOLA *from his pocket.*

LOLA *singing off*:

Doch denke immer — Achtung vor dem Raubtier
(For if you do you'll end up on the hook)

RATH *spreads the photographs of* LOLA *out on a tray in front of him.*

LOLA *singing off*: Nimm dich in Acht vor blonden Frauen

Die haben so etwas gewisses
(Take care of women who have blonde hair
They have a special flair)

Cut to a shot of the stage as LOLA, *her song finished, bows to loud applause and goes offstage. Return to* RATH, *who stubs out his cigarette, buttons his now slightly worn-looking coat, picks up the tray, and gets up slowly from his seat. A bowed figure, he wanders through the club, trying to sell the photographs, but he is met with catcalls. The camera pans after him for a few moments, as he makes his way among the audience.*

Medium shot of LOLA's *dressing room. In the foreground,* KIEPERT *is sprawled on a divan, smoking a cigar.* LOLA *enters and undoes her skirt. The general hubbub from the club itself can be heard in the background.*

Cut to RATH, *trying without success to sell his photographs to the audience. (Still on page 66)*

Back in the dressing room, LOLA *is sitting at the dressing table, applying cream to her face.* KIEPERT *is still smoking his cigar in the foreground.* RATH *enters, puts down the tray of photographs on a case and drains a half-empty glass of beer.* LOLA *crosses her legs, polishes her finger nails and starts to peel an apple.*

LOLA *with a hint of irony* : How's business?

RATH *putting down the glass* : Only two cards! What an ignorant bunch.

KIEPERT *jumping up* : An ignorant bunch! You're a fine one to talk! You'd do better to go and have a shave. What do you think you look like? RATH *takes a cigarette.* You can't expect to do any business looking like that. Yes, that's right, look dumb. . . . *His voice rises.* You're not at the university now!

He goes out, slamming the door. Insert of KIEPERT *outside the door, walking away. Inside the dressing room,* RATH *sits down behind* LOLA. *He has a glazed look.* LOLA *continues to peel her apple. (Still on page 66)*

LOLA : He's quite right, you know. You might at least let a razor see your face. Anyway, what's the matter with you? What do you have to call them an ignorant bunch for? After all, we make a living out of them.

LOLA *puts the apple peelings on the table, cuts a slice out of the apple and starts to eat it.*

RATH *in resignation and despair*: Oh yes! We make a living. We make a living!

LOLA: If you don't like it, you can always go.

RATH *mumbling*: Yes, I'll go away . . . I'm going . . . I'm going. . . . *He jerks upright, quivering, and shouts.* I've had enough! Enough! I'd rather die like a dog than carry on like this.

The camera pans rapidly as he rushes out of the room, slamming the door. Cut back to LOLA, *who has watched him go, smiling and munching her apple. Pan as she gets up and goes over to a gas-ring beside the door, which she lights, putting a pair of curling tongs on it to heat. She returns nonchalantly to her chair, puts one leg up on it and starts to take off her stocking. Long shot as the door of the dressing room opens slowly to admit a repentant* RATH. *He looks in an even more pitiful state than at the beginning of the scene. He shuts the door, and stands motionless in front of it.* LOLA *turns towards him, a contemptuous smile on her lips, and sits down on the divan.*

LOLA *as if nothing had happened*: Ah! . . . yes . . . pass me my stockings, will you?

RATH *gets the stockings, then kneels in front of* LOLA, *who stretches out her left leg. As he is pulling the stocking onto her leg, the bell rings to call her onstage.*

LOLA *pushing him*: Quick, get me the curling tongs.

RATH *goes to the gas-ring, while* LOLA *puts on the second stocking herself. He takes the tongs and hands them to* LOLA, *who has sat down again in front of the mirror. She takes the tongs, protests, and hands them back to* RATH.

LOLA *sharply*: But they're too hot!

RATH *looks around for something to bring down the heat. He goes up to a calendar hanging over the gas ring and tears off a sheet which spells out the day, 27. As he puts it on the tongs, it catches fire. He blows it*

*out and tears off another sheet marked 28. Close-up on
the calendar: three shots dissolve one into the other as
three more sheets are torn off, the last of which bears the
date 2 December, 1925. Dissolve to a close-up of a new
calendar, showing the year, 1929.*

In another dressing room, RATH *sits in medium close-up
at a dressing table lit by a flickering candle. He looks at
himself in the mirror with a disillusioned air. He is even
more unkempt than before and his forehead is covered
with wrinkles. He applies make-up laboriously, drawing
a vertical line through each eyebrow, then examines the
result in the mirror. (Still on page 67) Apparently
satisfied, he puffs at a cigarette, coughs, puts the cigarette
down and picks up a large, bulbous false nose. He puts
this on, and then a clown's wig. Looking sad and weary,
he checks his appearance once more in the mirror and
takes another puff at his cigarette. He then picks up a
very broad false collar, which is many times larger than
his neck, and passes it over his head.*

Pan to KIEPERT, *who comes up behind him wearing top
hat and tails. He has just emerged from a staircase, which
can be seen behind him with one of* LOLA'S *skirts hanging over the rail.*

KIEPERT : Well, Professor . . . And how are we to-day? *He
takes out a cigar and offers it to* RATH. You want a cigar?
It's Havana . . . the wrapper, Sumatra leaf!

LOLA *comes into view with a towel round her waist and
busies herself in the background.* RATH *takes the cigar
and smells it, turning as he does so towards the candle
so that one can see that his make-up is like the* CLOWN'S
in the beginning, in ' THE BLUE ANGEL.'

RATH *wearily* : You seem in a very good mood to-day.

KIEPERT : As well I might be . . . I have a very good
reason . . .

RATH *mouths a vague 'Ah!,' while* LOLA, *in the background, turns her head towards the two men.*

KIEPERT : You should be pleased too . . . You're becoming
my star.

LOLA *genuinely indignant* : Don't make fun of the old man.

94

He hasn't done anything to you.

KIEPERT: You can just shut up! . . . Your husband has become a very important part of the act. Look . . . *He takes something out of his pocket.*

LOLA *has come towards* KIEPERT. *Her face appears near his hand, which is brandishing a piece of paper.*

KIEPERT *partly off*: A contract! . . . All arranged by telegram. *A pause.* And where do you think it's for?

A new shot shows LOLA *reading the contract with interest, while* KIEPERT *turns towards* RATH.

KIEPERT: At ' THE BLUE ANGEL.'

RATH *starts imperceptibly, puffs at his cigarette, and raises his head slowly to look at* KIEPERT.

RATH: ' THE BLUE ANGEL '?

KIEPERT: Yes, we're going back to your home town. *Raising his arms.* There'll be lots of publicity : ' Professor Immanuel Rath.'

RATH *hotly*: Never! . . . I will never go back to that town!

KIEPERT *somewhat surprised*: You must think about it . . .

RATH: I already have!

KIEPERT: Isn't that just like you? For five years you've lived off this woman . . . *He indicates* LOLA, *who is wiping her hands* . . . and now the first time you have the chance to make a bit for yourself . . . *Mincingly* . . . the Professor says, ' No, I won't go.'

A new shot of the three of them together. RATH, *in his clown's outfit, is still seated.*

LOLA *to* KIEPERT: Leave him alone . . . You know very well he'll go.

RATH: No, I won't go!

KIEPERT: We're leaving tomorrow. It's all fixed.

RATH *quivering*: No, I won't go. Never! You can demand what you like of me, but that . . . I won't do it!

LOLA *patting him on the shoulder*: There's no need to get worked up.

RATH *putting his cigar in his mouth*: No, no, I won't do it! Never!

LOLA *losing patience*: But you don't have to go!

RATH *not listening to her and looking at himself in the mirror*:

Never! ... Never! ...

It is evening in a street. Medium close-up of a man with his back to the camera, passing a poster of 'LOLA-LOLA' on the wall. He pastes the front of the poster and sticks diagonally across the lower half of it a label which reads in gold lettering: 'PERSONAL APPEARANCE OF PROFESSOR IMMANUEL RATH.'

Behind the scenes in THE BLUE ANGEL, *the camera tracks sideways past the dressing rooms, following a couple of performers. In the foreground are nets, columns and beams. Nearby, the* PROPRIETOR *of* THE BLUE ANGEL *is standing against a column, saying goodbye to the outgoing performers, and welcoming the first arrivals from* KIEPERT's *troupe.* KIEPERT, *a cigar between his teeth, comes up to him.*

KIEPERT *very sure of himself*: Good morning, Herr Direktor.

PROPRIETOR: Good morning to *you*, Herr Direktor . . . You finally made it!

The two men shake hands and GUSTE *appears.*

GUSTE: 'Morning . . . Well, I never thought I'd be crawling about this hole again!

PROPRIETOR: My establishment . . . a hole?

Several girls greet the PROPRIETOR. *People pass continually in front of the camera.*

KIEPERT *with irony*: You haven't got any slimmer, I see.

PROPRIETOR: No, but you can hardly complain of that yourself.

A member of KIEPERT's *troupe enters the picture, raises his hat and greets the* PROPRIETOR.

PROPRIETOR: Good morning.

The performer goes off; the camera tracks along beside him.

KIEPERT: Why should I be losing weight? *Off.* Business is good. How are things with you?

PROPRIETOR *off*: Bah, we'll be all right now. The last three weeks though . . . I've never seen anything like it! No, Sir!

The camera has arrived at the entrance to the dressing rooms. The strong man MAZEPPA *comes out, wearing an overcoat and carrying a suitcase on his shoulder. He* passes in front of the camera, which pans after him. MAZEPPA goes up to the PROPRIETOR and KIEPERT.

MAZEPPA : Au revoir, Herr Direktor. *(Still on page 67)*

PROPRIETOR : Be seeing you, Maestro — but not in the next ten years, I hope. *He turns away disdainfully.*

MAZEPPA *somewhat put out and very haughty* : Your tin-pot establishment may be all right for the usual run of second-rate turns . . . but not for a high-class act like mine ! . . .

> *Cut to* LOLA *coming into the club. She is dressed in a fur coat, the collar of which is turned up against the snow falling outside.*
>
> *Return to* KIEPERT, MAZEPPA *and the* PROPRIETOR.

MAZEPPA *in French* : Au revoir, mon petit . . . cochon !

> *He goes off.*

KIEPERT *to the* PROPRIETOR : And who was that turn?

PROPRIETOR : Oh him ! . . . One more week with him and I'd have been bankrupt.

> *Cut to* LOLA *coming in through the doorway.* MAZEPPA *stands back to let her through, following her with his eyes.*

MAZEPPA : Good morning, Lola !

LOLA *off* : Good morning.

> MAZEPPA *stands for a moment looking after* LOLA, *who has gone by. Instead of going out of the door, he unloads his suitcase.*
>
> LOLA *has arrived between* KIEPERT *and the* PROPRIETOR. *She looks at the two men, then in the direction of* MAZEPPA.

LOLA : So many handsome men in one place.

KIEPERT *shrugging* : Good hunting !

> *He moves out of frame, while* LOLA *puts her hands on her hips and looks provocatively towards* MAZEPPA. *Cut to* MAZEPPA, *who smiles and raises his hat. Cut back to* LOLA, *who turns and goes towards the entrance to the dressing rooms.*

GUSTE *off* : Don't put all the cases on top of each other . . . Oh ! I've never seen anything like it . . . All over the floor !

> LOLA *pauses in the doorway, turns to smile at* MAZEPPA, *and goes in. Cut back to the* PROPRIETOR *as* MAZEPPA

passes him.

PROPRIETOR : Don't miss the train !

MAZEPPA *with a contemptuous grimace* : What do you know about love?

Medium shot of LOLA *in her dressing room, arranging her hair in front of a mirror. A noise is heard. Cut to* MAZEPPA, *who appears in the doorway and goes boldly towards the staircase leading up to the bedroom. He stops and smiles at* LOLA. *In another shot,* LOLA, *after noticing* MAZEPPA, *adjusts her coat and goes towards him. A new shot shows the pair of them at the foot of the stairs. (Still on page 68)* MAZEPPA *stands back to let her go up. She looks at him while, with an air of complicity, he raises his hat in a sweeping gesture.*

MAZEPPA *in French* : Permettez-vous, Madame . . . *In German* . . . Allow me to introduce myself. Mazeppa, Hans Adelbert Mazeppa.

LOLA *leaning back and smiling at him* : Yes . . . so what?

MAZEPPA *leaning on the stair-rail* : I'm staying here . . . for you ! That's how I am . . . a man of action ! *He raises himself on the rail and tries to kiss her.*

LOLA *pushing him back* : Don't be so impetuous ! . . . *Seductively.* We've got plenty of time . . . haven't we?

She smiles at him and goes up the stairs. MAZEPPA *gazes after her in fascination and then cups his hands to his mouth.*

MAZEPPA : For me, it's not a question of hours !

It is evening. A medium shot from above shows the entrance to THE BLUE ANGEL. *A* POLICEMAN *is standing in front of the door, holding back a noisy crowd.*

POLICEMAN : Now then . . . go home quietly . . . All the seats are sold . . .

A band strikes up. Dissolve to a shot of LOLA *and* MAZEPPA *behind the scenes in the club.* MAZEPPA *is carrying a bunch of flowers and smoking a cigar. He smiles at* LOLA, *who smiles back. They move on.*

In a long shot of the stage, six girls are seen dancing in a line, each one with her hand on the hips of the girl in front. There are loud cries from the audience.

AUDIENCE *shouting off*: The Professor! ... The Professor! ...
LOLA *appears, hands on hips. Smiling at the band she moves to the middle of the stage and starts to sing.*
LOLA *singing*: Take care of women who have blonde hair
> They have a special flair
> They have no way of being fair
> They'll strip you and leave you bare

Medium shot of LOLA *behind the line of girls.*
> Stare all you please but do no more than look
> For if you do you'll end up on the hook
> Take care of women with blonde hair
> They have a certain flair

A high shot of the audience shows the club completely full. The audience applauds.

Medium close-up of RATH *in* LOLA'S *dressing room. He is sitting inert in front of the mirror.* KIEPERT'S *hands come into view. He spreads make-up on* RATH'S *wrinkled forehead.* RATH *does not react, but closes his eyes from time to time.*

KIEPERT *partly off*: This will be the decisive evening of your career. To-day, if we're well received, we'll be a success! ... La Scala! ... Berlin! The Alhambra! ... London! ...

A new shot shows RATH *still seated, while* KIEPERT *stands over him, making him up as a clown.* GUSTE *is standing by the mirror.*

KIEPERT *to* GUSTE: The brush! ... GUSTE *hands it to him.* The Hippodrome! ... New York! ...

GUSTE: Stop romancing! You're getting delusions of grandeur. Right now, we're at 'THE BLUE ANGEL.'

KIEPERT: You're just a killjoy!

GUSTE: And what do you think you are?

KIEPERT: Stop squawking! Where's the nose?

He puts the clown's collar on RATH.

GUSTE: The nose?

KIEPERT: That's what I said, the nose. You had it, didn't you?

GUSTE: I had it? You had it, you mean!

KIEPERT *taking the nose from the box which* GUSTE *is holding*: I had it, did I?

99

GUSTE *to* RATH : There's no need to get nervous, ducky. I know exactly how you feel. I was just like you, just as nervous, twenty years ago . . . the evening I had my first big success.
KIEPERT *putting the false nose on* RATH : Will you shut your mouth for a few minutes?

Pan towards the door. The PROPRIETOR *rushes in.*

PROPRIETOR : Chairs! . . . More chairs! . . . Even the Mayor is here! *He goes out.*

GUSTE *proudly* : The Mayor! . . . Then I'm going out there, too! *She goes out.*

The PROPRIETOR *reappears, carrying two chairs.*

PROPRIETOR : Now there's no need to get nervous, Professor. We're sold out! . . . Everybody's here! Your colleagues, your pupils, everyone! What a crowd!

He moves out of the picture, while the camera stays on RATH *and* KIEPERT.

KIEPERT : Quite right! He's absolutely right. Keep calm. Look at me, for example. Now we'll go out and really give them the works!

He slaps RATH *on the shoulder and moves out of shot. The camera holds on* RATH, *who sits staring into space, utterly depressed. Outside the dressing room, a fireman and a stage hand stand in front of* LOLA'S *door, while the girls from the revue hurry past followed by* LOLA *and* MAZEPPA. *Back in* LOLA'S *dressing room,* RATH *is still sitting motionless in front of the mirror. He does not react when the girls enter and pass through the room* LOLA *and* MAZEPPA *come in. A new shot shows the three of them together,* RATH *sitting at the dressing table on which are a bottle of champagne and some glasses.* LOLA *looks at* RATH *and smiles at* MAZEPPA.

MAZEPPA *taking his cigar from his mouth and putting his arms round* LOLA : When I see a beautiful woman, I don't waste a minute. I'm well known for that!

LOLA lowers her eyes coquettishly. RATH *looks up, and* LOLA, *her head tilted slightly back, addresses him.*

LOLA : Well, what's the matter? What are you looking like that for? Every time I have a bit of fun, you act like a stuffed shirt!

100

MAZEPPA *putting his cigar back in his mouth* : What's going on here? The atmosphere's electric! Oh! . . . Well, it happens in the best of families. *To* RATH. Allow me to introduce myself. My name is Mazeppa . . . Hans Adelbert Mazeppa . . .

> RATH *does not look up.* LOLA *smiles arrogantly. The warning bell rings.*

LOLA *to* RATH : What are you sitting there for? Go on . . . go and do your number.

> MAZEPPA *picks up the bottle of champagne. (Still on page 85)* LOLA *moves out of the picture, but her reflection can still be seen in the mirror.*

MAZEPPA : Have some of this, my dear colleague. *He pours* RATH *a glass of champagne.* It can't do you any harm.

> *He takes the bottle and the second glass and moves out of frame. Cut to* LOLA *and* MAZEPPA *cautiously mounting the staircase which leads to* LOLA'S *bedroom.*

MAZEPPA : The boy seems a bit off!

> *Cut to* RATH, *who turns round with a glazed expression.* LOLA *laughs, off.* RATH *gets up and, seen in medium close-up, goes over to the staircase and looks up.* LOLA *laughs again, off.* MAZEPPA'S *voice is heard.*
>
> *In another shot of the dressing room,* RATH *still stands at the bottom of the staircase. The door opens and* GUSTE *appears. Through it can be heard music and the impatient shouts of the audience.*

GUSTE *intrigued* : What's going on? Where are you hiding? *She approaches* RATH. What's the matter with you?

> *Medium close-up of* RATH, *who turns towards her.*

GUSTE *off* : But . . . but what's the matter?

> *Medium shot of* GUSTE *looking at* RATH, *who is still standing at the bottom of the staircase.*

GUSTE : Lola, come down!

> *She moves out of sight. The camera stays on* RATH, *who shakes his head.*

RATH : I won't go onstage!

> *At these words,* KIEPERT *appears.*

KIEPERT : What's come over you? . . . Are you crazy? . . . You're not going to let me down now? . . . One minute before we have to go on. . . . You can't do that to me!

LOLA *comes slowly down the staircase. Medium close-up of her looking towards* RATH.

LOLA : What's the idea? . . . You don't want to go onstage?

Medium close-up of RATH, *completely distraught.*

LOLA *off* : You're going to go on.

LOLA *is seen taking the clown's wig from the table. She holds it out to* RATH.

LOLA : Put on your wig.

It is KIEPERT *who takes the wig from* LOLA *and puts it on* RATH'S *head. At that moment, the door opens to admit the* PROPRIETOR.

PROPRIETOR *furious* : What's this I hear? You don't want to go on?

KIEPERT : Yes, of course he'll go on!

PROPRIETOR *to* RATH : Have you gone mad? That kind of thing just doesn't happen in my establishment.

KIEPERT *pushing* RATH *towards the door* : Come on, move!

RATH, *looking completely shattered, turns towards* LOLA.

PROPRIETOR : Outside!

RATH *is pushed towards the door. Medium close-up of* LOLA *watching him. She looks sad and distressed.*

RATH, KIEPERT *and the* PROPRIETOR *are seen at the door of the dressing room.* RATH, *supported by the two other men, turns once more towards* LOLA, *while* KIEPERT *straightens his top hat for him. Cut to* LOLA, *hands on hips, walking nonchalantly across the room with a cold and disdainful smile. Return to* RATH, *now standing in the wings supported by* GUSTE *and the* PROPRIETOR. *There is a fanfare and applause. (Still on page 85)*

Cut to KIEPERT, *going onto the stage.*

In a long shot of the stage seen from the front, KIEPERT *draws aside the curtain and addresses the audience.*

KIEPERT : Ladies and Gentlemen! Please excuse this short interruption. A slight technical hitch! *Derisive shouts from the audience, mixed with laughter and applause.* But you will be amply recompensed by our next number . . . a display of conjuring which is truly international in character! *Shouts of* 'Bravo!' *and applause, as the curtain opens and the house lights go down.* In this number, I should like to present to you, as an altogether exceptional attraction, a man whom you all know already through his long and remarkable educational activities . . . *Shouts of derision* . . . his educational activities at this town's university.

> *There are shouts from the audience, particularly cries of* ' Onstage, Professor ! ' . . . ' Come on, Prof ! '
> *Close-up on* RATH *behind the curtain in the wings. He looks haggardly from the stage to the dressing room and back again. The audience continues to shout for* ' The Professor.'

KIEPERT *off* : I can see, Ladies and Gentlemen . . . *He appears before the camera* . . . that I need say no more. I shall therefore try your patience no longer. It is indeed our . . . *Long shot of the audience* . . . well-loved Professor Immanuel Rath ！

> *The audience reacts with laughter, whistles and applause. Cut to* RATH, *still standing at the side of the stage, looking towards the dressing room.* KIEPERT *comes and takes him by the arm.*

KIEPERT : Watch out now . . . or you'll mess up the whole number !

PROPRIETOR *agitated* : Come on ! Come on !

> KIEPERT *drags* RATH *away. The* PROPRIETOR *watches them go.* GUSTE *goes past the camera in the direction of the audience. In another shot, the* PROPRIETOR *is seen arriving at the bar. A long shot of the stage through transparent gauze curtains shows* KIEPERT *making his entrance and bowing.* RATH *appears at the back of the stage and* KIEPERT *indicates him to the audience. Another shot of* RATH *looking out through the transparent gauze curtains. As he moves slowly upstage, accompanied by shouts from the audience, he throws a glance in the direction of the dressing room.*
> *Medium shot of* LOLA *as she comes out of the dressing room and leans on the balustrade by the stage entrance.* MAZEPPA *follows her. Cut back to* RATH, *who turns back and continues to move upstage. Long shot of the audience, shouting and applauding. Return to* RATH, *as he draws aside the final curtain and comes out at the front*

*of the stage, his eyes wide, looking completely bewildered
by what is going on around him. Long shot of the stage
from the front.* KIEPERT *goes up to* RATH *and raises a
hand for silence. The audience falls quiet.*

KIEPERT : Ladies and Gentlemen, may I present to you . . .
Auguste, my apprentice sorcerer. *He indicates* RATH *and
hitches up his sleeves.* As you will observe, ladies and gentlemen, I work without props . . . only with my two hands . . .
my ten fingers. What I am going to show you, ladies and
gentlemen, is just a hat . . . a perfectly ordinary top hat. *He
takes* RATH's *hat from his head and shows it to the audience.*
No false bottom, no secret opening, no trap door. This hat,
ladies and gentlemen . . . I now place it . . .

Cut to LOLA *and* MAZEPPA, *seen from above. He tries to
kiss her; she is watching the stage.*

KIEPERT *continues off* : . . . on the head of my assistant
Auguste . . . *Cut back to the stage, seen from the front.* And
from the hat, I will make so bold as to produce for you, by
magic, here and now, a live dove! No doubt, ladies and
gentlemen, you are all convinced that the conjuror has already
put the dove inside the hat. Oh no! You are quite wrong.
*He turns the hat round, showing it to the audience from all
sides.* Look, I pray you . . . Empty! *He taps the hat.* Empty!
He taps on RATH's *head.* Quite empty!

*The audience is seen from above, laughing uproariously.
Resume on* KIEPERT, *who puts the hat back on* RATH's
head and goes over to a small table.

KIEPERT : One moment, please. Here is further proof! *He
brandishes a knife.* A knife, if you please!

Medium close-up on RATH *and* KIEPERT. KIEPERT
walks round RATH *and plunges the knife into the hat on*
RATH's *head several times.*

KIEPERT *plunging in the knife* : One . . . two . . . three . . .
four . . .

During this performance, RATH *looks at the audience
in bewilderment.* KIEPERT *returns to the table, exchanges
the knife for a pistol and comes back towards* RATH. *The
camera pans briefly to follow his movement.*

KIEPERT : Ladies and gentlemen . . . Do not be alarmed by

104

the sight of this revolver in my right hand. *He aims at* RATH'S *hat and fires, then goes and lifts the hat to reveal a dove perched on* RATH'S *head.* Voila! Now Auguste has got the bird!

Cut to a section of the audience, seen from the side. A man in top hat and tails gets up, looking angry and disgusted.

THE MAN : This is revolting! . . . Call the police!

VARIOUS VOICES : Sit down! . . . Sit down! . . .

Applause. The PROPRIETOR *is seen from above, sitting behind the bar. He smiles with satisfaction at the applause.*

PROPRIETOR *calling across to* KIEPERT : Herr Direktor, I've run out of eggs. Would you like to produce some magic ones for me?

Resume on KIEPERT, *who bows to the* PROPRIETOR, *while* RATH *glances into the wings.*

KIEPERT : Of course, Herr Direktor . . . Indeed, I shall be delighted to do so. Ladies and gentleman, I shall now make so bold as to produce some eggs, here and now . . .

While he is speaking, RATH *moves towards the wings. The camera catches him between the transparent gauze curtains, more bowed than ever. The audience laughs and whistles. Cut to* RATH'S *view down into the wings:* LOLA *is watching the stage, while* MAZEPPA *flirts with her. Cut back to* KIEPERT *as he catches up with* RATH.

KIEPERT : . . . from under my assistant's nose! *He tugs at* RATH'S *tail coat and speaks to him in an undertone.* Think what you're doing, Auguste . . . After all, you were once a schoolmaster! *Close-up on* RATH, *gazing stupidly.* No doubt, ladies and gentlemen, you are all convinced that friend Auguste has the eggs all ready inside his hat. A gross mistake! *He lifts the hat from* RATH'S *head to show a second dove.* Oh! Another bird . . .

Fanfares. The camera tilts down onto the audience, who are yelling and whistling, then returns to the two men on the stage. (Still on page 86)

KIEPERT : Right away, ladies and gentlemen . . . At your service! *He makes passes in front of* RATH'S *face.* One . .

two . . . three . . . hup! an egg. *He shows the egg to the audience, then turns to* RATH *and speaks to him in an undertone.* What's happened to your kick-a-rick-i? *Louder.* An ordinary common hen's egg . . . *He breaks it on* RATH'S *head.*

> *Group shot of the audience from above. Several people get up and leave in indignation. The majority laugh and clap.*

SHOUTS : Lay another one!

> *Cut back to the two men on the stage.*

SHOUTS *off* : Lay another one!

> *In another shot of the wings as seen by* RATH, LOLA *looks at the stage while* MAZEPPA *takes her in his arms and kisses her.* LOLA *keeps her eyes on the stage as he does so. Cut to the audience shouting 'Lay another one! ', then cut to* RATH *and* KIEPERT.

KIEPERT *to* RATH : If you don't crow this time, I'll finish you off. *Louder.* Once again, then!

> *He makes passes in front of* RATH'S *face.*

KIEPERT : One . . . two . . . three . . . An egg! *He shows it to the audience.* I'll prove he's laid an egg. *He breaks it on* RATH'S *head.*

> *Cut to the audience laughing, seen from above. Cut back to the two men.*

KIEPERT *losing his temper, but still keeping his voice down*: Crow, will you! . . . Kick-a-rick-i! If you don't crow now, I'll kill you! . . .

> *Cut to a close-up of* RATH *looking down. He has moved back slightly and is clinging to the curtain. Medium close-up from above of* LOLA *in* MAZEPPA'S *arms. They are still kissing.* LOLA *is looking onto the stage as before.* MAZEPPA *draws away and also looks up. Cut back to the stage.* KIEPERT *drags* RATH *violently away from the curtain and hauls him to the front of the stage.*

KIEPERT *brutally* : Crow.

> RATH *staggers, wild-eyed. Cut to* LOLA *and* MAZEPPA *looking up at the stage.* MAZEPPA *has an ironic smile on his lips. Return to the two men on the stage.* KIEPERT'S *face is set in a grim expression.* RATH, *staggering, crows hoarsely at the top of his voice like a madman. His*

106

crowing sounds mad, like a groan of despair. His hands tremble as he returns to the back of the stage and takes hold of the curtain, uttering another crowing as anguished as the first. He clings to the curtain and spins round, wrapping himself up in it. Medium close-up of KIEPERT, *who looks anxiously out at the audience. Medium shot of the stage from the front.*

RATH *seen through the curtains, bellowing*: Kick-a-rick-i!

The camera tilts down to a medium shot of LOLA *and* MAZEPPA. LOLA *is beginning to look really alarmed. The camera pans with her as she retreats towards her dressing room.*

MAZEPPA *watches her, then glances uneasily up at the stage. Medium shot of* RATH *as he parts the curtains and gazes down into the wings. In the background,* LOLA *can be seen going into her dressing room, followed by* MAZEPPA, *who glances several times in* RATH'S *direction and shuts the door behind him. Angry shouts can be heard from the audience. Cut to* RATH, *shot slightly from below, as he rushes down the steps from the stage and throws himself against the locked door of the dressing room. He batters the door with his head.*

RATH *bellowing*: Kick-a-rick-i!

He breaks open the door. There are shouts and whistles off from the audience, getting louder and louder.

Seen from inside LOLA'S *dressing room,* RATH *stands in the doorway and crows again, choking as he does so. In medium close-up,* LOLA *looks at him, anguished.*

LOLA: What's the matter with you? I haven't done anything!

Cut to MAZEPPA *watching* RATH *closely, then cut to* RATH.

RATH *puffing out his chest and bellowing*: Kick-a-rick-i!

He slams the door and leaps at LOLA. *Insert of* MAZEPPA, *surprised, then a medium shot of* RATH, *who throws himself on* LOLA *and tries to strangle her. She screams loudly, her screams mingling with* RATH'S *repeated crowing. In his madness,* RATH, *gripping* LOLA'S *throat, knocks her head against a suitcase, then against the piano, and drags her to the nearby divan, still throttling her.*

107

(Still on page 87) MAZEPPA *intervenes and hauls him off. There is a short battle which ends in* RATH, *the stronger of the two, throwing* MAZEPPA *furiously against the piano. Then, still crowing madly, he rushes into the chorus girls' dressing room where* LOLA *has taken refuge.* LOLA *screams off.*

Her screams continue as the camera cuts to KIEPERT *and the* PROPRIETOR, *who have come into the dressing room. They walk across and enter the other room. A chorus girl rushes out, followed by all the other girls. There is general confusion.* MAZEPPA *and the various members of* KIEPERT'S *troupe are gathered round the door as* LOLA *rushes out, terrified.* GUSTE *appears beside* MAZEPPA, *who leans against the wall, smiling with relief. The* PROPRIETOR *springs at him waving his arms. The fireman forces his way through the crowd. Furious voices are heard. Bystanders enquire what is going on. In the background, a dishevelled* LOLA *looks frantically at the staircase, then retreats slowly up it backwards, her face frozen in terror. A new group shot centred on* MAZEPPA *shows him opening a large trunk. He takes out a straitjacket which he uses in his act and comes back to the doorway.* GUSTE, *looking in alarm at what she sees in the room beyond, draws back to let him pass . . . The* PROPRIETOR *rushes out calling for a doctor.* GUSTE *goes out of the dressing room. The* PROPRIETOR *shuts the door behind her, then goes back into the room where* RATH *is. Fade out.*

Close-up on RATH *in the straitjacket, pale-faced with a vacant expression, his hair in disorder. He raises his head and looks slowly around him. Cut to* KIEPERT *outside the door. He hesitates, then makes up his mind and goes in. Return to* RATH *in a corner of the room, imprisoned in the straitjacket. He is gazing blankly at the floor, but turns towards* KIEPERT *on hearing the door open. His face suddenly changes, showing fear. Cut to* KIEPERT, *who shuts the door behind him and comes purposefully towards* RATH. *Medium shot of* RATH, *who closes his eyes and rests his head against the wall.*

Cut to KIEPERT *untying* RATH.

KIEPERT: Come here!

KIEPERT *undoes the straitjacket and throws it on the floor.*

KIEPERT: You asked for it! . . . I don't understand you . . . After all, you're an educated man! . . . And all that for the sake of a woman!

RATH *looks at him almost sympathetically, while* KIEPERT *pats him reassuringly on the shoulder.*

KIEPERT: Just take it easy . . . I'll take care of everything . . .

He gives RATH *a final pat on the shoulder and goes off. Another shot of* KIEPERT *by the door, as he turns to look at* RATH *before going out of the room. Cut back to* RATH, *who has watched him depart. His face has changed, the weary expression giving way to one of cunning as he sees his coat hanging up. The camera pans to follow his hands as they reach up and take the coat. It pans down again to show* RATH *putting on his coat, looking anxiously at the door. He then puts on his battered hat, and hurries to the door.*

Outside the dressing room, the door opens and RATH'S *face appears. He looks from side to side. Laughter and applause come from the audience.* RATH, *in medium close-up, looks out at the audience while* LOLA *is heard singing off.*

LOLA *singing off*: Falling in love again
       Never wanted to
       What am I to do? . . .

Medium shot of LOLA, *sitting astride a chair in the middle of the stage, which is hung with white drapes, but otherwise empty. She is wearing a close-fitting black costume and a broad-brimmed black hat; she sits astride the chair as she sings.*

LOLA *singing*: Can't . . .

Emphasising each word.

       . . . help it!
       I know I'm not . . .

She leans back, still holding onto the back of the chair.

       . . . to blame . . .

Long shot of RATH *as he slips away, looking back all the time over his shoulder. He moves out of the picture.*

LOLA *off* : Love's always been my game
        Can't help it!

Cut back to LOLA *as she leans forward with a crooked smile and, propping one arm on the back of the chair, caresses her shoulder with the other hand. (Still on page 87)*

LOLA *singing* : Men cluster to me
        Like moths around a flame
        And if their wings burn
        I know I'm not to blame.

She continues to sing.

        Falling in love again *(Still on page 88)*
        Never wanted to
        What am I to do?
        Can't help it!

Medium shot of RATH *sidling along the wall of the club towards the exit. He is half bending down and hiding his face. The camera pans after him, while the audience is heard applauding.*

Cut back to LOLA, *leaning on her chair and smiling down at the audience with a cool expression.*

It is night, as RATH *staggers down a narrow and ill-lit street, stopping frequently to support himself against the wall. The camera pans after him as he approaches a small square with a fountain in the foreground. A foghorn echoes, sinister in the distance. Exhausted,* RATH *stops and leans against the wall of a building, and laboriously scrapes away the thin coating of snow on it. He moves off again, staggering drunkenly. The foghorn is heard again.* RATH'S *shadow looms across a wall as the scene begins to fade.*

Dissolve to a long shot, from above, of the entrance to the high school. It is night. RATH, *seen from the back, staggers towards the porch and rings a bell. Close-up of the bell ringing. In medium shot,* RATH *rings again impatiently.*

Down the dark staircase of the school, a flickering light

comes towards the camera. *A limping* CARETAKER *appears in the foreground carrying a lamp. Cut back to* RATH *outside. The door opens and the lamp lights up his face as he enters. Pan as he passes in front of the* CARETAKER *and goes unsteadily up the stairs, followed by the latter and lit from below by the beam of his lamp. Medium shot of* RATH *advancing down the corridor to his classroom, leaning against the wall for support. He gets there with difficulty, opens the door and enters.*

Cut to the CARETAKER *following* RATH *in surprise up the staircase. Music. A second shot shows the* CARETAKER *arriving in the corridor. The light of his lamp falls on the half-open door of the classroom. He advances and hesitates for a moment, while the music changes to an orchestrated version of the tune played by the town clock, ' Be always faithful and honest.'*

Medium close-up of RATH *in his classroom. He is sitting sprawled over his desk. In the light of the lamp, he appears inert; but with his arms wide apart, he is gripping the edge of the desk in a final spasm. Between his arms, his head rests lifeless on the desk. The* CARETAKER *appears. Close-up of* RATH *followed by a medium shot of both. The* CARETAKER *panics and tries with all his might to release* RATH'S *hand from the grip on the desk, but in vain. Close-up of the hand, as the* CARETAKER *tries vainly to pull it away. In medium close-up, the* CARETAKER *looks at the dead* RATH *in horror and retreats to the door. The music stops abruptly. The final scene shows the inert slumped figure of* RATH, *lit by the* CARETAKER'S *lamp, (Still on page 88) gripping the corner of his desk in his last gesture to regain security. He has found peace in the classroom he once abandoned. The camera tracks slowly backwards disclosing the empty desks of his pupils, while outside the clock tolls twelve. On the final stroke of twelve, the words: THE END*